Tjef Sema Paut n Neteru
"The Movement Towards Union with the Gods and Goddesses"

The
Ancient Egyptian Yoga Exercise and
Meditation Movement Postures
For
Spiritual Health and Enlightenment

Seventh Edition – Expanded

"HER NAME IS HEALTH, SHE IS THE
DAUGHTER OF
EXERCISE,
WHO BEGOT HER ON
TEMPERANCE"
(Ancient Egyptian Proverb)

Cruzian Mystic Books
P.O.Box 570459
Miami, Florida, 33257
(305) 378-6253 Fax: (305) 378-6253

First U.S. edition 1996
Third Edition © 1998 By Reginald Muata Ashby

Fourth Edition © 1999

Fifth Edition © 2000

Sixth Edition © 200

Seventh Edition © 2005

Ashby, Muata
Egyptian Yoga Tjef Neteru Postures ISBN: 1-884564-10-0

Library of Congress Cataloging in Publication Data

1 Yoga, 2 Exercise, 3 Egyptian Philosophy 4 African Mythology, 5 Meditation, 6 Health, 7 Self Help.

Cruzian Mystic Books
Interned site – www.Egyptianyoga.com

Also by Muata Ashby

Egyptian Yoga: The Philosophy of Enlightenment
Initiation into Egyptian Yoga: The Daily Spiritual Program

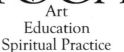

EGYPTIAN YOGA™
Art
Education
Spiritual Practice

Sema Institute of Yoga / Temple of Aset

Sema ($\frac{1}{4}$) is a Kamitic (Ancient Egyptian) word and symbol meaning *union*. The Sema Institute is dedicated to the propagation of the universal teachings of spiritual evolution which relate to the union of humanity and the union of all things within the universe. It is a non-denominational organization which recognizes the unifying principles in all spiritual and religious systems of evolution throughout the world. Our primary goals are to provide the wisdom of ancient spiritual teachings in books, courses and other forms of communication. Secondly, to provide expert instruction and training in the various yogic disciplines including Ancient Egyptian Philosophy, Christian Gnosticism, Indian Philosophy and modern science. Thirdly, to promote world peace and Universal Love.

A primary focus of our tradition is to identify and acknowledge the yogic principles within all religions and to relate them to each other in order to promote their deeper understanding as well as to show the essential unity of purpose and the unity of all living beings and nature within the whole of existence.

The Institute is open to all who believe in the principles of peace, non-violence and spiritual emancipation regardless of sect, race, or creed.

Sema Institute
P.O. Box 570459, Miami, Fla. 33257
(305) 378-6253, Fax (305) 378-6253
©2001

Health Note:

Before exercising with this program or the video,
consult your physician if you have high blood pressure, orthopedic problems, or
any other illnesses, bodily pains or discomforts, or if you are pregnant.
The reader agrees not to hold Drs. Muata or Dja (Karen) Ashby personally, or
Cruzian Mystic Books, or The Sema Institute of Yoga responsible for any injuries or physical impairments that may result. Exercise at your own risk.

The Journey of Ra

The First Movement of Thef Neteru

Table of Contents

The Sema Institute	3
PART I: What is Yoga?	7
The Paths of Yoga	8
What is Egyptian Yoga?	11
Part II: Origins of the Yoga Postures in Ancient Egypt and India	19
PART III: The Myth Behind the Ancient Egyptian Postures	37
The Creation	39
The Battle of Horus and Set	45
PART IIII: The Mystical Symbolism of The Characters in the Ausarian (Osirian) Myth	47
Asar (Osiris)	48
Set	49
Aset (Isis)	50
Nebethet (Nephthys)	52
Anubis	54
Sebek	56
Heru	56
Horus	57
Horus and Set	57
Djehuti (Thoth)	61
PART IIIII: Healthy Life Style, Diet and Nutrition, Preventative Health and Daily yoga Practices	63
The Ancient Egyptian Diet and Medical System	64
The Teachings of the Temple of Isis and the Diet of the initiates	67
The Daily Schedule for Yoga Practice	79
PART IIIIII: The Exercises, Yoga Postures and Meditations	86

Tjef neteru Sema Paut Neteru system Integral Path	90
Tjef neteru Sema Paut Neteru system Integral Path and Mystical Religion	91
The Special Concept of Phases in the Egyptian Yoga Thef Neteru System	92
Tjef Neteru as A Dynamic System of Varied Modes of Spiritual Practice	97
Pose 1: Time Before The Beginning	99
The Sitting Poses	100-101
Proper Breathing	102-103
Alternate Nostril Breathing	104-105
Pose 2: Nefertem	106-107
Pose 3: Nun	108-109
Pose 4: The Shu Pose	110-111
Pose 5: Warm Up	112-113
Pose 6: The Journey of Ra Posture Series	114-121
Pose 7-8: The Geb Shoulder-stand,	122-125
Pose 9: The Wheel Pose	126-127
Pose 10: The Fish Pose	128-129
Pose 11: The Spinal Twist Pose	130-131
Pose 12: The Forward Bend Pose	132-133
Pose 13: The Scorpion Pose	134-135
Pose 14: The Crocodile Pose	136-137
Pose 15: The Cobra Pose	138-139
Pose 16: The Sphinx Pose	140-141
Pose 17: Heru	142-143
Pose 18: The Jubilation Pose	144-145
Pose 19: Nut, the Heavens	146-147
Pose 20: Maat, righteousness/order	148-149
Pose 21: Aset-The Isis Pose	150-151
Pose 22: The Aset Throne Sitting	152-153
Pose 23: The Divine Embrace	154-155
Pose 24: Djed-Establishment	156-157
Pose 25: The Headstand	158-159
Pose 26: The Scarab	160-161

Table of Contents, Continued

Practice Questions	167
Working with the Postures	172
Egyptian Yoga Exercise Video Series	174
Egyptian Yoga Teacher Training	175
Other books and Videos by the authors	177

Part I
Introduction
What is Yoga?

What is Yoga? The literal meaning of the word YOGA is to *"YOKE"* or to *"LINK"* back. The implication is: to link back individual consciousness to its original source, the original essence, that which transcends all mental and intellectual attempts at comprehension, but which is the essential nature of everything in CREATION: Universal Consciousness. In a broad sense Yoga is any process which helps one to achieve liberation or freedom from the bondage of human existence. So whenever you engage in any activity with the goal of promoting the discovery of your true self, be it studying the wisdom teachings, practicing them in daily life, practicing exercises to keep the mind and body healthy for meditation, rituals to lead the mind toward the divine or meditation on the divine, you are practicing yoga. If the goal is to help you to discover your essential nature as one with God or the Supreme Being or Consciousness, then it is yoga.

The disciplines of Yoga fall under five major categories. These are: *Yoga of Wisdom, Yoga of Devotional love, Yoga of Meditation, Tantric Yoga* and *Yoga of Selfless Action.* Within these categories there are subsidiary forms which are part of the main disciplines. The important point to remember is that all aspects of yoga can and should be used in an integral fashion to effect an efficient and harmonized spiritual movement in the practitioner. Therefore, while there may be an area of special emphasis, other elements are bound to become part of the yoga program as needed. For example, while a yogin may place emphasis on the yoga of wisdom, they may also practice devotional yoga and meditation yoga along with the wisdom studies.

So the practice of any discipline that leads to oneness with Supreme Consciousness is called Yoga. If you study, rationalize and reflect upon the teachings, you are practicing *Yoga of Wisdom.* If you meditate upon the teachings and your Higher Self, you are practicing *Yoga of Meditation.* If you practice rituals which identify you with your spiritual nature, you are practicing *Yoga of Ritual Identification.* If you develop your physical nature and psychic energy centers, you are practicing *Serpent Power (Kundalini or Uraeus) Yoga.* If you practice living according to the teachings of ethical behavior and selflessness, you are practicing *Yoga of Action* in daily life. If you practice turning your attention toward the Divine by developing love for the Divine, you are practicing *Devotional Yoga* or *Yoga of Divine Love*. The practitioner of yoga is called a yogin (male practitioner) or yogini (female practitioner) and one who has attained the culmination of yoga is also called a yogi. In this manner yoga has been developed into many disciplines which may be used in an integral fashion to achieve the same goal: Enlightenment. Enlightenment is the state of consciousness of complete harmony of mind, body and spirit wherein one discovers one's true identity and union with the Divine. Enlightenment also implies the discovery of one's innermost Self, the immortal and eternal elements of one's being beyond the mortal and transitory human personality and body. Therefore, the aspirant should learn about all of the paths of yoga and choose those elements which best suit his/her personality or practice them all in an integral, balanced way.

Advancement in Yoga is dependent on the desire of the individual to put forth his/her effort in the direction toward self-improvement under proper guidance. In this way, the negative karma of the past which has created the present conditions can be destroyed in order to create prosperity and spiritual emancipation.

Most people have heard of Yoga as an exercise or as a strange and perhaps even occult practice, however, Yoga is a vast science of human psychology and spiritual transformation which includes the practice of virtuous living, dietary purification, physical exercises (asanas), breathing techniques, study of the wisdom teachings and their practice in daily life, and meditation. Through a process of gradually blending these in the course of ordinary life, an individual can effect miraculous changes in his/her life and thereby achieve the supreme goal of all existence, the goal of Yoga: Union with the Higher Self.

The teachings which were practiced in the ancient Egyptian temples were the same ones later intellectually defined into a literary form by the Indian Sages of Vedanta and Yoga. This was discussed in the book *Egyptian Yoga: The Philosophy of Enlightenment* by Dr. Muata Ashby. The Indian Mysteries of Yoga and Vedanta represent an unfolding and intellectual exposition of the Egyptian Mysteries. Also, the study of Gnostic Christianity or Christianity before Roman Catholicism will be useful to our study since Christianity originated in ancient Egypt and was also based on the ancient Egyptian Mysteries. Therefore, the study of the Egyptian Mysteries, early Christianity and Indian Vedanta-Yoga will provide the most comprehensive teaching on how to practice the disciplines of yoga leading to the attainment of Enlightenment. The question is how to accomplish these seemingly impossible tasks? How to transform yourself and realize the deepest mysteries of existence? How to discover "who am I?" This is the mission of Yoga Philosophy and the purpose of yogic practices.

In this form of study, we will use various new terms you may not have heard before, but we will make every effort to explain them in detail and to relate them to the Western understanding as well as to use the terms in the other religions that will be discussed. In this way the teaching will not only be relevant to the Egyptian Mysteries, but also to other religions as well. Therefore, if your previous background was in Christianity or in one of the various traditions within Hinduism, you will not have any difficulty in understanding the teachings as they will be presented. As you go through this volume, you will discover that each of the elements within Indian and Christian Yoga were practiced long ago in ancient Egypt.

What is Egyptian Yoga?

In order to better understand the perspective of ancient Egyptian mystical philosophy that will be presented in this volume, it will be necessary to establish the correct definitions which will be used to reference the various teachings and disciplines which will be discussed.

The ancient Egyptian language and symbols provide the first "historical" record of Yoga Philosophy and Religious literature. The Indian culture of the Indus Valley Dravidians and Harappans appear to have carried it on and expanded much of the intellectual expositions in the form of the Vedas, Upanishads, Puranas and Tantras, the ancient spiritual texts of India.

Egyptian Yoga is what has been commonly referred to by Egyptologists as Egyptian "Religion" or "Mythology", but to think of it as just a set of stories or allegories about a long lost civilization is to completely miss the greatest secrets of human existence. Yoga in all of its forms was practiced in Egypt earlier than anywhere else in our history. This unique perspective from ancient Africa provides a new way to look at life, religion and the discipline of psychology. Perhaps most importantly though, Egyptian mythology, when understood as a system of Yoga, gives every individual insight into their own divine nature. This is its true worth.

Above from left to right are the symbols of Egyptian Yoga. These are: *Sma, nfr, nkh, htp.* The hieroglyph **"Sema"**, represented by the union of two lungs and the trachea, symbolizes the union of the Higher and lower self, the duality, which leads to the knowledge of the One, indivisible cosmic consciousness.

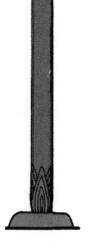

The hieroglyph ⎯ **"Nefer",** close in pronunciation to **"Neter"** (God)**,** expressed by the union of the heart and the trachea symbolizes: that which is the most beautiful thing, the highest good, the greatest achievement.

The hieroglyph ♀ **"Ankh,"** symbolizes the union of the male (cross-temporal) and the female (circle-eternal) aspects of oneself, leading to the transformation into an androgynous being. Thus, the two become One. The Ankh was also later used in Christianity and Hinduism as a symbol of divinity. Therefore, the Ankh is the unifying symbol which links Egypt, India and Christendom.

The hieroglyph ⎯ **"Hetep"**, symbolizes supreme peace, the final abode of all who satisfy the desire of their soul, union with the Higher Self: YOGA.

Egyptian Yoga encompasses many myths and philosophies which lead to the reunion of the individual soul with its Higher Self. Ancient Egyptian religion involves three major theological branches based on the primordial Trinity (*Amun-Ra-Ptah*) which emanates out of the *hidden* and *nameless* transcendental Divinity. This Divinity is variously known under the following names: *Nameless One, Neberdjer (Nebertcher) , Shetai, Tem, Neter Neteru, Amun, Asar (Osiris), Ra, Heru (Horus), Kheper, and Aset (Isis)*. These names are to be understood as being synonymous since they refer to the same idea of an *Absolute Supreme Being* and transcendental reality from which the phenomenal world arises as land rises out of an ocean.

Besides Asar (Osiris) and Aset (Isis), the central and most popular character within the ancient Egyptian Religion of Asar (Osiris) is Heru (Horus) who is an incarnation of his father, Asar (Osiris). Asar (Osiris) was killed by his brother, who out of greed and Setian (demoniac) tendency, craved to be the ruler of Egypt. With the help of Djehuti, the God of wisdom, his mother Aset (Isis), and Hetheru (Hathor), his consort, Heru (Horus) prevails in the struggle against Set for the rulership of Egypt. Heru's (Horus') struggle symbolizes the struggle of every human being to regain rulership of the Higher Self and to subdue the

lower self. With this understanding, the land of Egypt is equivalent to the Kingdom/Queendom of Heaven concept of Christianity. Therefore, the union of Upper and Lower Egypt is a subtle reference to the union of the lower self and the Higher Self within a human being. The struggle toward the unification of these is the central issue of the conflict between Heru (Horus) and Set, the rulers of Upper and Lower Egypt, respectively.

The most ancient writings in known history are from the ancient Egyptians. These writings are referred to as hieroglyphics and they refer to the religion of Asar (Osiris) and Heru (Horus). Also, the most ancient civilization known was the ancient Egyptian civilization. The proof of this lies in the ancient *Sphinx* which has now proven to be over 12,000 years old. The original name given to these writings by the ancient Egyptians is *Metu Neter* meaning "the writing of God" or "Divine Speech". These writings were inscribed in temples, coffins and papyruses and contain the teachings in reference to the spiritual nature of the human being and the ways to promote spiritual emancipation, awakening or resurrection from ordinary human consciousness and mortality to cosmic consciousness and immortality.

Smai Tawi
(From Chapter 4 of
the *Prt m Hru*)

The Term "Egyptian Yoga" and The Philosophy Behind It

As previously discussed, Yoga in all of its forms were practiced in Egypt apparently earlier than anywhere else in our history. This point of view is supported by the fact that there is documented scriptural and iconographical evidence of the disciplines of virtuous living, dietary purification, study of the wisdom teachings and their practice in daily life, psychophysical and psycho-spiritual exercises and meditation being practiced in Ancient Egypt, long before the evidence of its existence is detected in India (including the Indus Valley Civilization) or any other early civilization (Sumer, Greece, China, etc.).

The teachings of Yoga are at the heart of *Prt m Hru*. As explained earlier, the word "Yoga" is a Sanskrit term meaning to unite the individual with the Cosmic. The term has been used in certain parts of this book for ease of communication since the word "Yoga" has received wide popularity especially in western countries in recent years. The Ancient Egyptian equivalent term to the Sanskrit word yoga is: ***"Smai."*** Smai means union, and the following determinative terms give it a spiritual significance, at once equating it with the term "Yoga" as it is used in India. When used in conjunction with the Ancient Egyptian symbol which means land, ***"Ta,"*** the term "union of the two lands" arises.

In Chapter 4 and Chapter 17 of the *Prt m Hru,* a term "Smai Tawi" is used. It means "Union of the two lands of Egypt," ergo "Egyptian Yoga." The two lands refer to the two main districts of the country (North and South). In ancient times, Egypt was divided into two sections or land areas. These were known as Lower and Upper Egypt. In Ancient Egyptian mystical philosophy, the land of Upper Egypt relates to the divinity Heru (Horus), who represents the Higher Self, and the land of Lower Egypt relates to Set, the divinity of the lower self. So ***Smai Taui*** means "the union of the two lands" or the "Union of the lower self with the Higher Self. The lower self relates to that which is negative and uncontrolled in the human mind including worldliness, egoism, ignorance, etc. (Set), while the Higher Self relates to that which is above temptations and is good in the human heart as well as in touch with transcendental consciousness (Heru). Thus, we also have the Ancient Egyptian term ***Smai Heru-Set,*** or the union of Heru and Set. So Smai Taui or Smai Heru-Set are the Ancient Egyptian words which are to be translated as "**Egyptian Yoga.**"

Above: the main symbol of Egyptian Yoga: *Sma.* The Ancient Egyptian language and symbols provide the first "historical" record of Yoga Philosophy and Religious literature. The hieroglyph Sma, ⚕ "Sema," represented by the union of two lungs and the trachea, symbolizes that the union of the duality, that is, the Higher Self and lower self, leads to Non-duality, the One, singular consciousness.

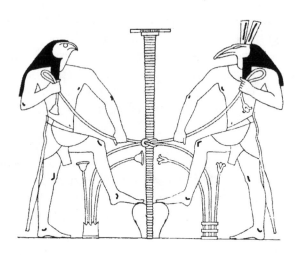

(†)

(±)

More Ancient Egyptian Symbols of Yoga

Above left: Smai Heru-Set,

Heru and Set join forces to tie up the symbol of Union (Sema –see (B) above). The Sema symbol refers to the Union of Upper Egypt (Lotus) and Lower Egypt (Papyrus) under one ruler, but also at a more subtle level, it refers to the union of one's Higher Self and lower self (Heru and Set), as well as the control of one's breath (Life Force) through the union (control) of the lungs (breathing organs). The character of Heru and Set are an integral part of the *Pert Em Heru.*

The central and most popular character within Ancient Egyptian Religion of Asar is Heru, who is an incarnation of his father, Asar. Asar is killed by his brother Set who, out of greed and demoniac (Setian) tendency, craved to be the ruler of Egypt. With the help of Djehuti, the God of wisdom, Aset, the great mother and Hetheru, his consort, Heru prevailed in the battle against Set for the rulership of Kemet (Egypt). Heru's struggle symbolizes the struggle of every human being to regain rulership of the Higher Self and to subdue the lower self.

The most ancient writings in our historical period are from the Ancient Egyptians. These writings are referred to as hieroglyphics. The original name given to these writings by the Ancient Egyptians is *Metu Neter,* meaning "the writing of God" or *Neter Metu* or "Divine Speech." These writings were inscribed in temples, coffins and papyruses and contained the teachings in reference to the spiritual nature of the human being and the ways to promote spiritual emancipation, awakening or resurrection. The Ancient Egyptian proverbs presented in this text are translations from the original hieroglyphic scriptures. An example of hieroglyphic text was presented above in the form of the text of Smai Taui or "Egyptian Yoga."

Egyptian Philosophy may be summed up in the following proverbs, which clearly state that the soul is heavenly or divine and that the human being must awaken to the true reality, which is the Spirit, Self.

"Self knowledge is the basis of true knowledge."

"Soul to heaven, body to earth."

"Man is to become God-like through a life of virtue and the cultivation of the spirit
through scientific knowledge, practice and bodily discipline."

"Salvation is accomplished through the efforts of the individual.
There is no mediator between man and {his/her} salvation."

"Salvation is the freeing of the soul from its bodily fetters, becoming a God through knowledge and wisdom, controlling the forces of the cosmos instead of being a slave to them, subduing the lower nature and through awakening the Higher Self, ending the cycle of rebirth and dwelling with the Neters who direct and control the Great Plan."

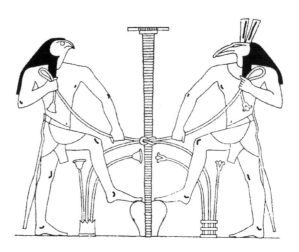

Smai Tawi
"Egyptian Yoga"

Part II
Origins of the Yoga Postures in Ancient Egypt and India

ORIGINS OF THE YOGA POSTURES

History Of The Yogic Postures in Ancient Egypt and India

Since their introduction to the West the exercise system of India known as "Hatha Yoga" has gained much popularity. The disciplines related to the yogic postures and movements were developed in India around the 10th century A.C.E. by a sage named Goraksha.* Up to this time, the main practice was simply to adopt the cross-legged meditation posture known as the lotus for the purpose of practicing meditation. The most popular manual on Hatha Yoga is the **Hatha-Yoga-Pradipika ("Light on the Forceful Yoga).** It was authored by Svatmarama Yogin in mid. 14th century C.E.**

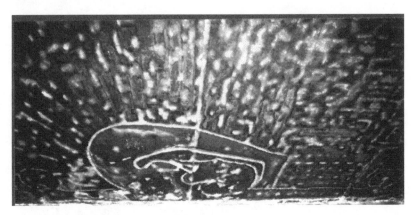

Plate 1: Above- The god Geb in the plough posture engraved on the ceiling of the antechamber to the Asarian Resurrection room of the Temple of Hetheru in Egypt. (photo taken by Ashby)

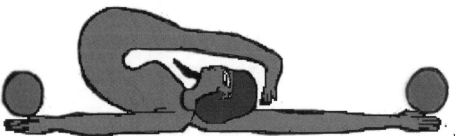

Prior to the emergence of the discipline the physical movements in India just before 1000 A.C.E., a series of virtually identical postures to those which were practiced in India can be found in various Ancient Egyptian papyruses and inscribed on the walls and ceilings of the temples. The Ancient Egyptian practice can be dated from 300 B.C.E 1,580 B.C.E. and earlier. Exp. Temple of Hetheru (800-300 B.C.E.), Temple of Heru (800-300 B.C.E.), Tomb of Queen Nefertari (reigned 1,279-1,212 BC), Temple of Horemakhet (10,000 B.C.E.) and various other temples and papyruses from the New Kingdom Era 1,580 B.C.E). In Ancient Egypt the practice of the postures (called *Sema Paut* (Union with the gods and goddesses) or *Tjef Sema Paut Neteru* (movements to promote union with the gods and goddesses) were part of the ritual aspect of the spiritual myth which when practiced serve to harmonize the energies and promote the physical health of the body and direct the mind, in a meditative capacity, to discover and cultivate divine consciousness. These disciplines are part of a larger process called Sema or *Smai Tawi* (Egyptian Yoga). By acting and moving like the gods and goddesses one can essentially discover their character, energy and divine agency within one's

*Yoga Journal, {The New Yoga} January/February 2000, *The Shambhala Encyclopedia of Yoga* by Georg Feuerstein, Ph. D.
***Hatha-Yoga-Pradipika,** *The Shambhala Encyclopedia of Yoga* by Georg Feuerstein, Ph. D.

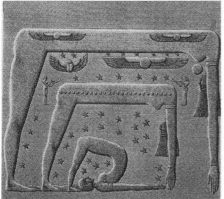

consciousness and thereby also become one of their retinue, i.e. one with the Divine Self. In modern times, most practitioners of Hatha Yoga see it as a means to attain physical health only. However, even the practice in India had a mythic component which is today largely ignored.

Plate 2: Nut and Geb and the higher planes of existence. Below: -line drawing of the same scene. (photo taken by Ashby-Temple of Aset (Isis)) See Arrow.

The figure above depicts another conceptualization of the Netherworld, which is at the same time the body of Nut in a forward bend posture. The innermost goddess symbolizes the lower heaven where the moon traverses, the physical realm. The middle one symbolizes the course of the sun in its Astral journey. This shows a differentiation between the physical heavens and the Astral plane, as well as time and space and Astral time and space, i.e., the concept of different dimensions and levels of consciousness. The outermost symbolizes the causal plane. Geb, who is in the plough posture, symbolizes the physical plane and all solid matter, while the goddesses represent the subtler levels of existence.

Records of <u>meditation as a discipline for lay people, as opposed to priests</u>, first show up about 500 B.C. in both India and China. Contrary to what many Yoga students believe, his (Patanjali) text said little about Hatha Yoga postures, which weren't a widespread practice at the time. It only speaks of a sitting posture for the practice of meditation and nothing more.

From Raja Yoga Sutras – Translated by Swami Jyotirmayananda:
Samadhi Pad Sutra 46: *seated pose for meditation*
Samadhi Pad Sutra 48-49: *perfecting the seated pose for meditation*

Plate 3: The Egyptian Gods and Goddesses act out the Creation through their movements (forward bend (Nut), spinal twist (Geb), journey of Ra and the squatting, standing motion (Shu and Nun).

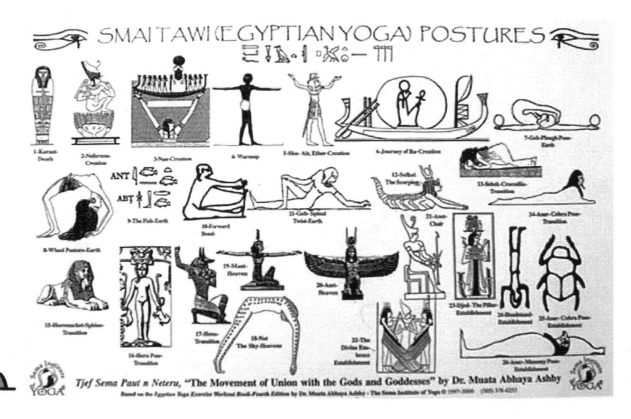

Figure 1: The varied postures found in the Kemetic papyruses and temple inscriptions. (Egyptian Yoga Postures Poster)

Figure 2: The practice of the postures is shown in the sequence below. (Egyptian Yoga Postures Poster by Muata Ashby)

Figure 3: Below- the Goddess Parvati from India, practicing the tree Pose – modern rendition.

Many people do not know that when the practice of Hatha Yoga was adopted by yogis (one who studies the yoga disciplines) in India in the first millennium A.C.E., it was repudiated by the established practitioners.* When it was opened up to the general community and ceased to be a practice of secluded yogis and was later brought to the west at the turn of the 20th century much later, it was not quickly adopted. However, in the latter part of the 20th century, due to the ardent promotion by a few Indian masters, it has gained wide notoriety. However, for the most part only the physical benefits have been adopted and acknowledged while the mystical teachings within the discipline have not been embraced generally. Beyond the misinformed and the dogmatic followers of orthodox religion, who repudiate yoga as an occult, evil practice, one comment by a famous personality in late 20th century western culture typifies the feeling of the vast majority of those who are involved in yoga for the physical "benefits" other than "spiritual" aspects of yoga:

"I don't want it to change my life, just my butt."

-famous actress (United States-2000 A.C.E.)**

Still, it must be understood that many people who are leading a worldly life are first introduced to yoga through the discipline of the postures in ordinary sessions dedicated to promoting physical health and later turn towards the spiritual aspects. However, there is much concern among advanced practitioners of Yoga in India and elsewhere, that Western culture has appropriated yoga and converted it to something other than yoga as it has been known for thousands of years. Instead of having Geb or Parvati as the role models, such prominent (worldly) personalities as actors and entertainers Julia Roberts, Madonna, Woody Haroldson and others have become the "ideal." So now, the same materialistic pursuits (physical health, beauty, sex-appeal, excitement, etc.), which are the hallmarks of western culture, have been projected on yoga by westerners who have appointed themselves as the purveyors of yoga to the masses. Many also distribute a myriad of products which are not necessary or desirable for the practice of yoga postures such as spandex, props, lotions, bikini yoga, etc., and conduct not spiritual yoga retreats but yoga vacations, yoga parties and the like. Yoga originated as a non-

*_The Shambhala Encyclopedia of Yoga_ by Georg Feuerstein, Ph. D.
**Yoga Journal, {The New Yoga} January/February 2000

secular spiritual discipline for transcending the world and has now been converted by many into a means to enjoy the worldly pleasures more intensely. This deviation from spiritual discipline to an instrument for enhancing worldly pleasure-seeking is perhaps most prominently visible in the discipline of Tantra Yoga. Using sexual symbolism to drive home a mystical teaching, Tantra Yoga has less to do with physical sexual intercourse between human beings than intercourse of the soul with the Divine. Yet, many so called practitioners of Tantra Yoga in the west tirelessly promote the idea that it is a form of "Sex-Yoga" designed to attain spiritual enlightenment and the heights of worldly pleasure at the same time. There are many misconceptions about the history and teaching of yoga and this is perhaps one of the most blatant. The hedonistic* path of life, which typifies western culture, has been shown to be ultimately a dead end street leading to frustration and regret in later life. Yet people follow blindly the inane statements of ignorant religious leaders, entertainers, politicians, marketers and advertisers, which lead to spiritual and worldly bankruptcy.

Many practitioners of the Hatha Yoga postures do not realize that the postures were not designed just to promote physical health. Actually, like the Kemetic system, the Hindu Yoga posture system is also designed to relate a human being to the gods and goddesses and the cosmic forces, which are symbolized by the use of animal names and visualizations using natural objects. This is accomplished by the practice of the movements, study of the mythology and philosophy behind them and meditative absorption with the principles and energies that they represent. The promotion of health is only a means to an end, a byproduct of the practice, and not an end in itself. The ultimate goal of yoga is to awaken the spiritual consciousness. Any other use of yoga is a misuse or at least a limited use. In these respects the movement systems of Kemet from Ancient Egypt, Yoga from India, and Kung Fu of China, are unique when compared to other forms of exercise, movement systems. Western forms of exercise are designed to cultivate the external muscles and physical energy while the Eastern and African disciplines are designed to develop and cultivate the internal life force, which transcends physicality and the world itself.

The table on page 28 shows the dates in which the practice of spiritual postures was enjoined in Africa and Asia. The earliest recorded evidence for the practice of specific movements that lead to spiritual enlightenment occurs in Ancient Egypt (Kamit) c. 10,000 B.C.E. The earliest recorded practice in India of the yoga postures is c. 1,000 A.C.E.

NOTES:
Yoga Journal, {The New Yoga} January/February 2000

*he·don·ism (hēd′n-ĭz′əm) n. 1. Pursuit of or devotion to pleasure, especially to the pleasures of the senses. 2. *Philosophy.* The ethical doctrine holding that only what is pleasant or has pleasant consequences is intrinsically good.

THE YOGIC POSTURES
IN ANCIENT EGYPT AND INDIA

Hatha-Yoga-Pradipika, *The Shambhala Encyclopedia of Yoga* by Georg Feuerstein, Ph. D.
The Shambhala Encyclopedia of Yoga by Georg Feuerstein, Ph. D.
The Shambhala Encyclopedia of Yoga by Georg Feuerstein, Ph. D.
Yoga Journal, {The New Yoga} January/February 2000

Kemetic (Egyptian) Cobra

Indian Full Cobra

Kemetic Wheel

Indian Wheel

Kemetic Spinal Twist

Indian Spinal Twist

Kemetic Lotus

Indian Lotus

A History of the Discipline of Physical Postures in Ancient Egypt and India from Ancient to Modern times

Smai Tawi Tjef Neteru Yoga Practice in Ancient Egypt	Hatha Yoga Practice in Ancient India and the dates when introduced
1 Horemacket (Sphinx 10,000 B.C.E.) 2 18th Dynasty Papyri 1580 B.C.E. 3 Tomb of Hatshepsut 1580 B.C.E. 4 Temple and Tomb of Seti I (reigned 1306-1290) 5 Tomb of Queen Nefertari (reigned 1,279-1,212 BC), 6 Temple of Heru (800-300 B.C.E.), 7 Temple of Aset (800-300 B.C.E.) 8 Temple of Hetheru (400-300 B.C.E.) 9 Independent Mystery traditions (3rd century to 20th century. 10 Tjef Neteru Sema Paut (Movement of the Gods and Goddesses) 20th century *Women practiced the postures since the most ancient times.	1 **Sage Goraksha** 10th century A.C.E. (First Introduced) 2 *Hatha-Yoga-Pradipika ("Light on the Forceful Yoga).* It was authored by Svatmarama Yogin in mid. 14th century C.E. 3 **Shiva Samhita** – Hatha Yoga text –melds Vedanta with Hatha 1750 A.C.E. 4 Women first admitted to Hatha Yoga practice (Late 19th century **Modern Practices in India and the West** 1 **Ananda Yoga** (Swami Kriyananda) 20th Century 2 **Anusara Yoga** (John Friend) 20th Century 3 **Ashtanga Yoga** (Pattabhi Jois) 20th Century 4 **Bikram Yoga** (Bikram Choudhury) 20th Century 5 **Integral Yoga** (Swami Satchidananda) 20th Century 6 **Iyengar Yoga** (B.K.S. Iyengar) 20th Century 7 **Kripalu Yoga** (Amrit Desai) 20th Century 8 **Kundalini Yoga** (Yogi Bhajan) 20th Century 9 **Sivananda Yoga** (Swami Vishnu-devananda) 20th Century 10 **Svaroopa Yoga** (Rama Berch) 20th Century 11 **TriYoga,** (Kali Ray) 20th Century 12 **Viniyoga** (T.K.V. Desikachar) 20th Century

Table on next page: A Timeline of the Discipline of Physical Postures in Ancient Egypt and India

Thus it is evident that the practice of the Yoga postures in Egypt began over 2500 years before the practice commenced in India. It is also likely that the Indians were introduced to the system when they connected with the Ancient Egyptians during the period of the reign of the Indian Sage King Ashoka. (See the book *African Origins of Civilization, Religion and Yoga Spirituality* by Muata Ashby.)

It has been suggested that the practice of the Hatha Yoga in India began with the use of the Lotus, which may be traced to the Indus Valley culture. Also, the use of the term "Asana" or posture, by the Indian Sage Patanjali, who wrote the classical yoga treatise "Yoga Sutras" which are also known as "Ashtanga Yoga" or eight legged path or steps of yoga. The use of the lotus pose in the Indus Valley culture seems only to relate to the iconography of meditation. This is also true for the Yoga Sutras. Patanjali refers to asana as a means to practice effective meditation and not as a concerted system and series of postures for promoting health and the development of the inner Life Force. Thus, Hatha Yoga as we know it today began at the end of the first millennium of our era and not in the time before the Common Era (B.C.E.). So Ancient Egypt appears to be the source for the discipline of postures. These were practiced by the priests and priestesses in order to promote physical health but more so to promote a meditative state of mind that would allow them to come closer to the cosmic forces represented by the divinities in the iconography of the postures, thereby allowing them to discover their own divine essence and ultimately the source of all the cosmic forces, the Supreme Self.

20th Century A.C.E.

1. **Ananda Yoga** (Swami Kriyananda)
2. **Anusara Yoga** (John Friend)
3. **Ashtanga Yoga** (K. Pattabhi)
4. **Ashtanga Yoga** (Pattabhi Jois)
5. **Bikram Yoga** (Bikram Choudhury)
6. **Integral Yoga** (Swami Satchidananda b.
7. **Iyengar Yoga** (B.K.S. Iyengar)
8. **Kripalu Yoga** (Amrit Desai)
9. **Kundalini Yoga** (Yogi Bhajan)
10. **Sivananda Yoga** (Swami Vishnu-devananda)
11. **Svaroopa Yoga** (Rama Berch)

Women first admitted to Hatha Yoga practice

1893 A.C.E. — World Parliament of Religions – Vedanta Introduced to the West

1750 A.C.E. — Shiva Samhita – Hatha Yoga text –melds Vedanta with Hatha

1539 A.C.E — Birth of Sikhism

1350 A.C.E. — Hatha Yoga Pradipika text -India

1000 A.C.E. — Goraksha – Siddha Yogis First Indian Hatha Yoga Practice

600 A.C.E. — Birth of Islam

Year 0 — Birth of Jesus – Christianity ✝

300 B.C.E. — Arat, Geb, Nut Egyptian Yoga Postures – Late Period

1,680 B.C.E. — Geb, Nut, Ra, Asar, Aset, Sobek Egyptian Yoga Postures – New Kingdom

2,000 B.C.E. — Indus Valley – Kundalini – Serpent Power-Lotus Pose

3,600 B.C.E. — Nefertem Egyptian Yoga Posture – Old-Middle Kingdom Period

10,000 B.C.E. — Serpent Power-Horemakhet Egyptian Yoga Posture – Ancient Egyptian

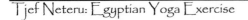

The Physical Yoga Postures Part 2

Contrary to popular knowledge, the practice of the discipline that was later known as "Hatha Yoga" in India began at around the year 1000 A.C.E. and not in pre-Christian (Comma Era) times as is commonly supposed. Often times the mention of the word "asana" in the Patanjali Yoga Sutras" (200 B.C.E.) is thought to represent an early practice of Hatha Yoga. However, when the statements by Patanjali are examined closely, it is clear that the meaning relates to a sitting posture for meditation and not the elaborate system of a sequence of postures designed to cultivate physical health and harmonization of the Ha (solar) and Tha (lunar) energies of the physical and astral bodies of a person.

Further, notice that the popular practices of Hatha Yoga which have come to the West are all 20th century developments. They are outgrowths of the original Hatha Yoga concept but are modern interpretations, exemplifying elaborate and in many ways intricate concepts and practices which were not enjoined by sage Goraksha. The emphasis on the physical postures as either a discipline for physical health in a limited sense or as a self-contained end of Yoga at the exclusion of the other disciplines (meditation, study of the wisdom teachings, right action, devotional worship) has prompted many Indian masters to complain about the disregard for the true meaning of Yoga and the true purpose of the exercise postures. As with so many other disciplines, Western society has taken cultural disciplines and traditions but ascribing new meanings and transforming these disciplines and traditions into something other than what they originally were. The practice of the Indian Hatha Yoga postures has been adopted by many in the western countries but the adjunct practice of meditation and the philosophy of the postures has been left aside in great measure. The postures are mostly used as a meas to promote physical health as opposed to their original intent of promoting positive spiritual evolution. The following article illustrates this point. (text emphasis by Ashby)

TAKE A SEAT by Alan Reder
If your not meditating, are you really doing Yoga?
– **Yoga Journal Feb. 2001**

THE SUCCESS OF YOGA in the West may have come at a heavy price. <u>Many teachers worry that something special has been lost in Yoga American style</u>, and that something is meditation. Meditation, not postures, is the heart of Yoga, they point out. <u>In Patanjali's India, Yoga and meditation were nearly synonymous, yet</u> <u>meditation plays only a minor role in many American Yoga courses. In others, it is not taught at all.</u>

<u>Some Yoga students regard meditation as boring cultural baggage</u> and appreciate learning postures without it. But what if your experience with Yoga has inspired you to go deeper, into Yogic spirituality? If your Yoga teacher doesn't offer meditation guidance, how should you begin? <u>Since Yoga comes from India</u>, should your meditation technique be Hindu or Buddhist? Is Zen Buddhist okay? Does the inner peace you already feel in Yoga class count?

Records of <u>meditation as a discipline for lay people, as opposed to priests,</u> first show up about 500 B.C. in both India and China.

Contrary to what many Yoga students believe, his (Patanjali) text said little about Hatha Yoga postures, which weren't a widespread practice at the time.

The important question arises, is Yoga *(Exercise)* in the West really being practiced correctly? In fact, can it even be said that yoga is being practiced in the west? The following excerpts from an article that appeared in the magazine Yoga Journal, explores this problem.

"The New Yoga, America is Reinventing the Practice…But it is still Yoga?"
"New Light on Yoga" – Yoga Journal – July/Aug 1999

"Dr. Jayadeva Yogendra…his father, at the turn of the twentieth century, was one of the first yogic crusaders to bring hatha yoga to practices ….and begin teaching them to a lay audience. 'When I see what yoga has become I the west,'….. **'I wish my father had left it with the hermits in the caves'."**

The degradation of the practice of Yoga was typified by the comment of a well known Hollywood Actress:

"I don't want Yoga to change my life, just my butt!"
USA – 2000 ACE

Many teachers of the Indian Yoga postures in the western countries take pride in learning the jargon of Sanskrit words and wowing their students with difficult contortions but not including philosophy or meditation in their practice, presumably because the populations of the west are hostile to forms of spirituality other than the western religions (Christianity, Islam, and Judaism). In the current climate (late 20th century-early 21st) where the social climate is increasingly religiously intolerant, the prospects of Yoga and other mystical traditions in the west will be problematical. The following guidelines should be followed if the true Indian and Ancient Egyptian tradition of the postures is to be upheld.

Integral Practice of the Yoga postures includes physical regimen, diet, philosophy, meditation, devotional practice and virtuous living.

- **Integral Practice is not just the Postures, not just meditation, not just cultivation of the vital body, not just wisdom**
- **It must include mystical philosophy, leading to entry into higher planes of existence.**
- **It is that experiences that informs all yogic movements in all religions of history.**
- **Names, jargons, clothing, memorized texts, etc. are foundations, not attainments.**

Hatha Yoga, Buddhism and Ancient Egypt

"In Zen Buddhism, for example, students can chant a lineage of teachers stretching back for centuries, with each Zen master certified by the one preceding. No such unbroken chain of transmission exists in hatha yoga. For generations, hatha yoga was a rather obscure and occult corner of the yoga realm, viewed with disdain by mainstream practitioners, kept alive by a smattering of isolated ascetics in caves and Hindu *maths* (monasteries). It appears to have existed for centuries in seed form, lying dormant and surfacing again and again. In the twentieth century, it had almost died out in India. According to his biography, Krishnamacharya had to go all the way to Tibet to find a living master…Given this lack of a clear historical lineage, how do we know what is "traditional" in hatha yoga? Where did our modern proliferation of poses and practices come from? Are they a twentieth century invention?"
-July/August 1999 By Anne Cushman (Yoga Journal)

Many practitioners of Indian Hatha Yoga are fond of describing their practice as "ancient" and as being comprised of an unbroken "lineage" of teachers going back "thousands of years." Upon close examination of the practice in India we find that no such unbroken chain of transmission exists in Hatha Yoga. Actually in the early twentieth century, it had almost died out in India.

> HATHA-YOGA ("forceful Yoga"), also called hatha-vidya ("science of hatha"); the type of Yoga specific to the Kanphata sect, though this designation is also applied in general to the vast body of doctrines and practices geared toward Self-realization by means of perfecting the body.

The term Hatha Yoga is defined as "forceful union," that is forcing spiritual evolution via the cultivation of the energies of the physical body. In Ancient Egypt the program of transformation through body cultivation was described in the Pert M Heru text, more commonly known as the Egyptian Book of the Dead, as well as in other texts.

The origins of Hatha Yoga were clearly in Buddhism and not in Hinduism since we find evidence of rejection of Hatha Yoga by the Hindu sages. **Hatha Yoga is clearly rejected in the Laghu -Yoga - Vasishtha (5.6.86, 92), which maintains that it merely leads to pain. Some of criticisms, especially against the magical undercurrents.**

> <u>**GORAKSHA or GORAKSHANATHA**</u> The most popular teacher of hathayoga, who is widely celebrated as its inventor, is Goraksha (9th or 10th cen. CE), a member of the Natha tradition, in which body cultivation played a crucial role. He is acclaimed by some as the first writer of Hindi or Punjabi prose and is credited with the authorship of numerous works, including the Goraksha-Samhit4, the Amaraugha-Prabodha, the Jnata-Amrita-Shastra, and the Siddha-SiddhantaPaddhati. Although the Tibetan sources speak of him as a Buddhist magician, the works ascribed to him and his school have a distinct leaning toward Shaivism.

> The most popular teacher of hathayoga, who is widely celebrated as its inventor, is **<u>Goraksha</u>** (9th or 10th cen. CE), a member of the Natha tradition, in which body cultivation played a crucial role. In India it came under attack early in its development. For instance, it is clearly rejected in the Laghu -Yoga - Vasishtha (5.6.86, 92), which maintains that it merely leads to pain. The most formidable critic of hatha-yoga was Vijndna Bhikshu, a sixteenth- century savant and Yoga practitioner. Some of his criticisms, especially against the magical undercurrents present in this yogic approach, are undoubtedly justified.

Tantric philosophy figures prominently in the origins of Indian Hatha Yoga as one of its disciplines. As was discussed in the section of this book entitled "Item for Comparison 11: Tantric Philosophy," Tantrism was practiced in Ancient Egypt from the earliest times. The practice of Tantrism in Ancient Egypt was akhnowledged by Ajit Mookerjee.

> Tantric influence, however, is not limited to India alone, and there is evidence that the precepts of tantrism traveled to various parts of the world, especially Nepal, Tibet, China, Japan and parts of South-East Asia; its influence has also been evident in Mediterranean cultures such as those of Egypt and Crete.
>
> -Ajit Mookerjee (Indian Scholar-Author –from the book *The Tantric Way*)

Specifically, Tantric Buddhism gave rise to the earliest practice of certain postures as a means to enhance spiritual evolution. Before this time, the only reference to Asana or posture was the sitting posture for meditation, mentioned in the Raja Yoga Sutras by Patanjali. Below: **Patanjali Yoga Sutras Sadhana Pad (200 B.C.E) - sutra 46: Asana – Trans. Swamiji Jyotirmayananda**

Sutra 46

स्थिरसुखमासनम्

STHIRA SUKHAM ASANAM.

STHIRA: Steady. SUKHAM: Comfortable. ASANAM: Pose (for meditation).

Meaning

A seated pose (for meditation) that is steady and comfortable is called *Asana*.

Explanation

To attain success in the practice of concentration, meditation and *Samadhi*, an aspirant begins by developing steadiness of a meditative pose.

There is clear evidence of the existence of the Sakkara/Memphis- School of Memphite Theology- Divinity *Ptah*. There is also clear evidence of the practice of "magi" or "Hekau" and the practice of Tjef Neteru or postures of the gods and goddesses in Egypt.

Buddhist records show that early Buddhists had visited Memphis and had set up a settlement there. Henceforth Buddhism begins to develop similar iconographies including the Divinity sitting on the lotus, and also lotus friezes similar to those of Ancient Egypt appear in Buddhist art.

Left: Heru on the Lotus, Right: Buddha on the Lotus

In the book Search for the Buddha by Charles Allen, the author documents the Buddhist connection to Ancient Egypt as follows. The Buddhist/Indian ruler had a practice of setting up pillars with inscriptions attesting to his following the Buddhist principles and other edicts. One was discovered that unequivocally shows that ancient Egypt and India were associated.

In March 1838 a more complete and accurate impression of the Girnar rock inscription became available to James Prinsep. On 14 'March he wrote another of those letters to Alexander Cunningham that bubble over with enthusiasm and good cheer. The Girnar inscription differed from the pillar edicts in a number of passages, and in one he had found a line that linked Piyadasi/Ashoka to Egypt and the Ptolemys:

The passage in the 14th edict is much mutilated, and I long for a more correct copy. It really becomes interesting to find Egypt and Ptolemy known to Asoka! I must give you the real text:

> *Yona raja paran cha tena chaptaro rajanan tulamayo*
> Greek king furthermore by whom the Gypta rajas Ptolemy
> *cha antigina cha maga cha * * **
> and Antigonus and Magus and * * *
> *savata devanampiya dhammanusasti anubatate yata pajati*
> everywhere Beloved of the God's religious precept reaches
> where goes.

Hurrah for inscriptions!

Here was proof of diplomatic links between Ashoka's empire and the West, in the form of Alexander the Great's successors: the Egyptian king Ptolemy was probably Ptolemy II (ruled 285-247 BCE); Antigonus was probably Antigonos Gonatos of Macedonia

TANTRIC BUDDHIST "MAGIC" YOGA begins to develop especially in Tibet – India. The following timeline indicates the early process of evolution of hatha yoga in India.

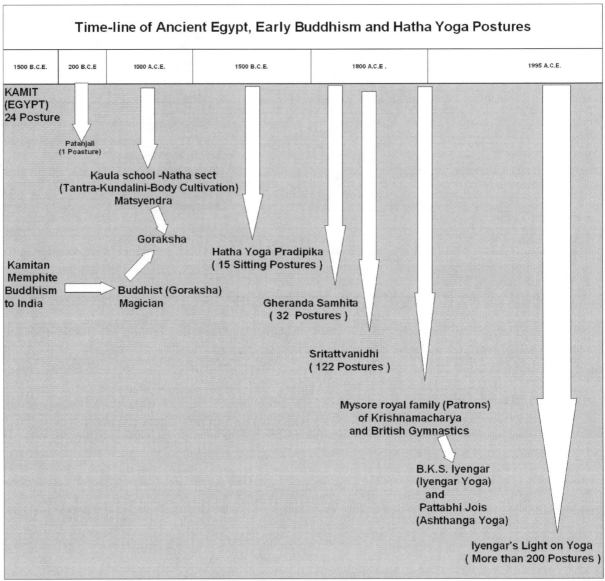

Time-line of Ancient Egypt, Early Buddhism and Hatha Yoga Postures

1500 B.C.E.	200 B.C.E	1000 A.C.E.	1500 B.C.E.	1800 A.C.E .	1995 A.C.E.

KAMIT (EGYPT) 24 Posture

Patanjali (1 Poasture)

Kaula school -Natha sect (Tantra-Kundalini-Body Cultivation) Matsyendra

Goraksha

Hatha Yoga Pradipika (15 Sitting Postures)

Kamitan Memphite Buddhism to India

Buddhist (Goraksha) Magician

Gheranda Samhita (32 Postures)

Sritattvanidhi (122 Postures)

Mysore royal family (Patrons) of Krishnamacharya and British Gymnastics

B.K.S. Iyengar (Iyengar Yoga) and Pattabhi Jois (Ashthanga Yoga)

Iyengar's Light on Yoga (More than 200 Postures)

In ancient Kamit there were at least 24 postures in the spiritual practice prior to the time of Patanjali. In the practice of Kamitan Tjef Neteru (Egyptian Hatha Yoga) the "magic" consists in using postures to engender certain alignments with spiritual energies and cosmic forces. This is the kind of practice repudiated by the Hindu sages and adopted by the Tantric Buddhists. Between the years 100 A.C.E. and 1000 A.C.E. the Buddhist Kaula school developed some postures. Then Goraksha developed what is regarded by present day Hatha Yoga practitioners as a practice similar to the present day. However, the number of postures only reached 15 at the time of the Hatha Yoga Pradipika scripture. The Mysore family was instrumental in the development since they were strong patrons of Hatha Yoga. Subsequent teachers developed more postures and vinyasa (which was not practiced in early Indian Hatha Yoga) up to the 20th century where there are over 200. The teacher Krishnamacharya said he had learned from a yoga teacher in Tibet. Krishnamacharya's first writings, which cited the Stitattvanidhi as a source, also featured vinyasa (sequences of poses synchronized with the breath) that Krishnamacharya said he had learned from a yoga teacher in Tibet. So the practice of the postures in India does not extend to ancient times and did not begin in India with Hinduism but with Buddhism and Buddhism was associated with the Ancient Egyptian city of Memphis where postures and spiritual magic were practiced previously.

The following table (on next page) shows the dates in which the practice of spiritual postures was enjoined in Africa and Asia. The earliest recorded evidence for the practice of specific movements that lead to spiritual enlightenment occurs in Ancient Egypt (Kamit) c. 10,000 B.C.E. The earliest recorded practice in India of the yoga postures is c. 1,000 A.C.E.

Timeline Summary (1800 B.C.E.-1000 A.C.E.)

1800 BCE Ancient Egypt – Discipline of Sema Paut-Egyptian Yoga Postures, Arat Shetaut Neter (Goddess Mysteries), Arat Sekhem (Serpent Power), Hekau ("Magic)
Already ancient

550 BCE Cambyses invades Egypt – Buddhism, Jainism, Pythagoreaninsm, Zoroastrianism, Confucianism, Taoism - BORN

100 ACE -Tantrism – Emerges as a Distinct culture of Spirituality in Hinduism, Buddhism and Jainism Emphasizing Shaktism (Goddess female energy and Goddess as female aspect of the Absolute), Occultism, Magic, Kundalini

c. 460-490 A.C.E. Shakta and Tantra Spirituality -Writings elaborating on Tantric spirituality and mysticism of the Chakras

Goraksha – Develops Hatha Yoga to "Force" the movement of Kundalini (serpent Power) # Postures ?
1000 ACE

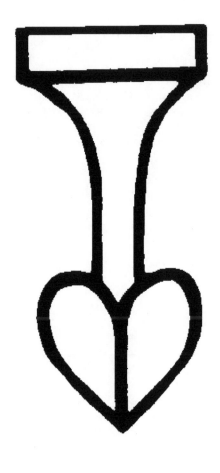

Part III
The Myth Behind the Ancient Egyptian Yoga Postures

YOGA EXERCISES IN ANCIENT EGYPT

Not many people are aware of the fact that the Ancient Egyptians practiced Yoga Exercises and Meditation thousands of years ago.

This enlightening book and the available video presentation, sheds light on the ancient myths of the gods and goddesses of Ancient Egypt and also provide a method of practicing physical exercise while meditating on the cosmic principles which the *Neters* (gods and goddesses) represent. This allows the practitioner of yoga to experience a psycho-physical and psycho-spiritual transformation leading toward the highest goal of human existence: Spiritual Enlightenment or the discovery of one's own Divinity and union with the Cosmos.

This presentation will look on exercise not just as a physical discipline for health of the body. True health is a result of an integrated relationship between the mind, body and spirit. What will make this presentation unique is the mystical aspect which will be imparted and practiced along with the physical exercises. There are many reliefs and steles displaying the Ancient Egyptian Gods and Goddesses in what has come to be known as Yoga Exercise Postures.

Yoga Postures are special exercises which engender a psycho-physical and psycho-spiritual transformation which leads to harmony of the mind, body and spirit. Throughout history, the teachings of Yoga have been associated with religion and mythology. In order to understand the deep psycho-spiritual symbolism of each exercise, it will be necessary to understand the creation myth of ancient Egypt and the Myth of Asar (Osiris). These teachings impart profound wisdom on the understanding of the soul, creation, and the journey of every human being through life.

A COMPENDIUM OF THE AUSARIAN RESURRECTION MYTH

THE CREATION

The process of creation is explained in the form of a cosmological system for better understanding. Cosmology is a branch of philosophy dealing with the origin, processes, and structure of the universe. Cosmogony is the astrophysical study of the creation and evolution of the universe. Both of these disciplines are inherent facets of Ancient Egyptian philosophy through the main religious systems or Companies of the gods and goddesses. A Company of gods and goddesses is a group of deities which symbolize a particular cosmic force or principle which emanates from the all-encompassing Supreme Being, from which they have emerged. The Self or Supreme Being manifests creation through the properties and principles represented by the *Pautti* Company of gods and goddesses - cosmic laws of nature. The system or Company of gods and goddesses of Anu is regarded as the oldest, and forms the basis of the Asarian (Osirian) Trinity. It is expressed in the diagram below.

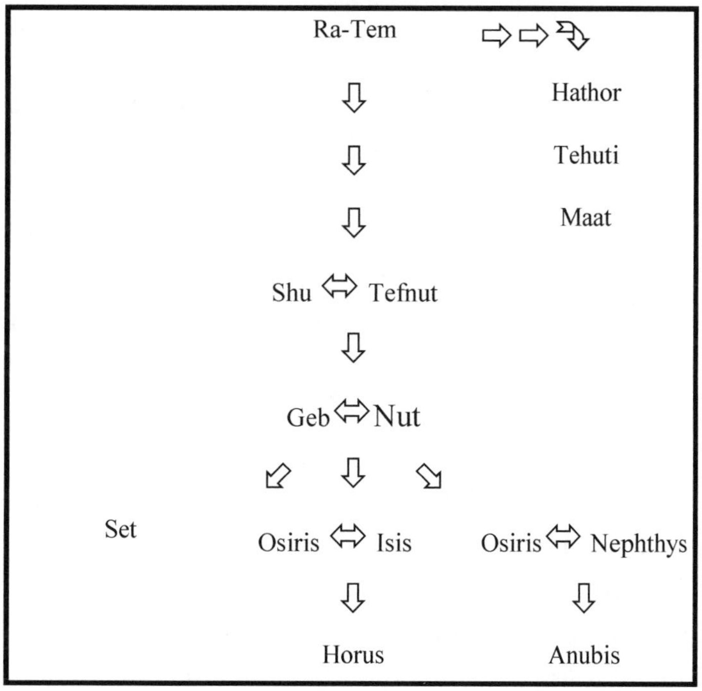

```
              Ra-Tem          ⇨ ⇨ ⇲

                 ⇩            Hathor

                 ⇩            Tehuti

                 ⇩             Maat

          Shu ⇔ Tefnut

                 ⇩

           Geb ⇔ Nut

        ⇗      ⇩      ⇘

  Set   Osiris ⇔ Isis    Osiris ⇔ Nephthys

             ⇩                    ⇩

           Horus               Anubis
```

The Creation: Ra emerges with the Neters
from the Primeval Waters-Nu.

The diagram above shows that the *Psedjet* (Ennead), or the creative principles which are embodied in the primordial gods and goddesses of creation, emanated from the Supreme Being. Ra or Ra-Tem arose out of the *"Nu"*, the Primeval waters, the hidden essence, and began sailing the *"Boat of Millions of Years"* which included the Company of gods and goddesses. On his boat emerged the "neters" or cosmic principles of creation. The neters of the Ennead are Ra-Atum, Shu, Tefnut, Geb, Nut, Asar (Osiris), Aset (Isis), Set, and Nebehet (Nephthys). Hetheru (Hathor), Djehuti and Maat represent attributes of the Supreme Being as the very *stuff* or *substratum* which makes up creation. Shu, Tefnut, Geb, Nut, Asar (Osiris), Aset (Isis), Set, and Nebehet (Nephthys) represent the principles upon which creation manifests. Anpu (Anubis) is not part of the Ennead. He represents the feature of intellectual discrimination in the Asarian

(Osirian) myth. "Sailing" signifies the beginning of motion in creation. Motion implies that events occur in the realm of time and space, thus, the phenomenal universe comes into existence as a mass of moving essence we call the elements. Prior to this motion, there was the primeval state of being without any form and without existence in time or space.

Asar, Aset and Heru

Asar (Osiris) and Aset (Isis) dedicated themselves to the welfare of humanity and sought to spread civilization throughout the earth, even as far as India and China.

During the absence of Asar from his kingdom, his brother Set had no opportunity to make innovations in the state because Aset was extremely vigilant in governing the country, and always upon her guard and watchful for any irregularity or unrighteousness.

Upon Asar's return from touring the world and carrying the teachings of wisdom abroad there was merriment and rejoicing throughout the land. However, one day after Asar return, through his lack of vigilance, he became intoxicated and slept with Set's wife, Nebehet . Nebehet, as a result of the union with Asar, begot Anpu .

Ra and the Company of Gods and Goddesses in the Barque of Millions of Years

Ra

Set, who represents the personification of evil forces, plotted in jealousy and anger (the blinding passion that prevents forgiveness) to usurp the throne and conspired to kill Asar. Set secretly got the measurements of Asar and constructed a coffin. Through trickery Set was able to get Asar to "try on" the coffin for size. While Asar was resting in the coffin, Set and his assistants locked it and then dumped it into the Nile river.

The coffin made its way to the coast of Syria where it became embedded in the earth and from it grew a tree with the most pleasant aroma in the form of a DJED. The DJED is the symbol of Asar's BACK. It has four horizontal lines in relation to a firmly established, straight column. The DJED column is symbolic of the upper energy centers (chakras) that relate to the levels of consciousness of the spirit within an individual human being.

The King of Syria was out walking and as he passed by the tree, he immediately fell in love with the pleasant aroma, so he had the tree cut down and brought to his palace. Aset (Auset, Ast), Asar's wife, the personification of the life giving, mother force in creation and in all humans, went to Syria in search of Asar. Her search led her to the palace of the Syrian King where she took a job as the nurse of the King's son. Every evening Aset would put the boy into the "fire" to consume his mortal parts, thereby transforming him to immortality. Fire is symbolic of both physical and mental purification. Most importantly, fire implies wisdom, the light of truth, illumination and energy. Aset, by virtue of her qualities, has the power to bestow immortality through the transformative power of her

The Continuous Process of Creation: Ra Traverses in His Barque over the Heavens (Nut).

symbolic essence. Aset then told the king that Asar, her husband, is inside the pillar he made from the tree. He graciously gave her the pillar (DJED) and she returned with it to Kamit (Kmt, Egypt).

Upon her return to Kmt Aset went to the papyrus swamps where she lay over Asar's dead body and fanned him with her wings, infusing him with new life. In this manner Aset revived Asar through her power of love and wisdom, and then they united once more. From their union was conceived a son, Heru, with the assistance of the gods Djehuti (Thoth) and Amun (Amon).

One evening, as Set was hunting in the papyrus swamps, he came upon Aset and Asar . In a rage of passion, he dismembered the body of Asar into several pieces and scattered them throughout the land. In this way it is Set, the brute force of our bodily impulses and desires, that "dismembers" our higher intellect. Instead of oneness and unity, we see multiplicity and separateness which give rise to egoistic (selfish) and violent behavior. The Great Mother, Aset, once again sets out to search, now for the pieces of Asar with the help of Anpu and Nebehet.

After searching all over the world they found all the pieces of Asar (Osiris)' body, except for his phallus which was eaten by a fish. In Eastern Hindu-Tantra mythology, the God Shiva, who is the equivalent of Asar, also lost his phallus in one story. In Ancient Egyptian and Hindu-Tantra mythology, this loss represents seminal retention in order to channel the sexual energy to the higher spiritual centers, thereby transforming it into spiritual energy. Aset, Anpu and Nebehet re-membered the pieces, all except the phallus which was eaten by the fish. Asar thus regained life in the realm of the dead, the Duat.

Heru, therefore, was born from the union of the spirit of Asar and the life giving power of Aset (physical nature). Thus, Heru represents the union of spirit and matter, and the renewed life of Asar, his rebirth. During this time of exile, Aset left Egypt and wandered around with the child in search of a place to be safe away from Set. While traveling through a town Heru was bitten by an evil scorpion which had been sent out by Set. The goddess Nebehet and the scorpion goddess Selket came to her assistance and cried with Aset . Then Selket told Aset to use her worlds of power to call

MAAT

upon Ra, the Supreme Being, to stop his movements in the Barque of Millions of Years and to restore Heru back to health. Ra sent Djehuti with words of power and spiritual energy to revive Heru. After Heru was nursed back to health and educated by his mother Aset (Isis) he quickly grew up to be a strong young man. As Heru grew up, Asar, who was abiding in the **Duat**, encouraged him to take up arms (vitality, wisdom, courage, strength of will) and establish truth, justice and righteousness in the world by challenging Set, its current ruler.

The Battle of Heru and Set

Shu

The battle between Heru and Set took many twists, sometimes one seeming to get the upper hand and sometimes the other, yet neither one gaining a clear advantage in order to decisively win. At one point Aset tried to help Heru by catching Set, but due to the pity and compassion she felt towards him she set him free. In a passionate rage Heru cut off her head and went off by himself in a frustrated state. Even Heru is susceptible to passion which leads to performing deeds that one later regrets. Set found Heru and gouged out Heru's eyes. During this time Heru was overpowered by the evil of Set. He became blinded to truth (as signified by the loss of his eyes) and thus, was unable to do battle (act with MAAT) with Set . His power of sight was later restored by Hetheru (goddess of passionate love, desire and fierce power), who also represents the left Eye of Ra. She is the fire spitting, destructive power of light which dispels the darkness (blindness) of ignorance.

When the conflict resumed, the two contendants went before the court of the Ennead gods (Company of the nine gods who ruled over creation, headed by Ra). Set, promising to end the fight and restore Heru to the throne, invited Heru to spend the night at his house, but Heru soon found out that Set had evil intentions when he tried to have intercourse with him. The uncontrolled Set also symbolizes unrestricted sexual activity. Juxtaposed against this aspect of Set (uncontrolled sexual potency and desire) is Heru in the form of ithyphallic (erect phallus) MIN, who represents not only the control of

sexual desire, but its sublimation as well. Min symbolizes the power which comes from the sublimation of the sexual energy.

Through more treachery and deceit Set attempted to destroy Heru with the help of the Ennead, by tricking them into believing that Heru was not worthy of the throne. Asar sent a letter pleading with the Ennead to do what was correct. Heru, as the son of Asar, should be the rightful heir to the throne. All but two of them (the Ennead) agreed because Heru, they said, was too young to rule. Asar then sent them a second letter (scroll of papyrus with a message) reminding them that even they cannot escape judgment for their deeds; they too will be judged in the end when they have to finally go to the West (abode of the dead).

This signifies that even the gods cannot escape judgment for their deeds. Since all that exists is only a manifestation of the absolute reality which goes beyond time and space, that which is in the realm of time and space (humans, spirits, gods, angels, neters) are all bound by its laws. Following the receipt of Asar's scroll (letter), Heru was crowned King of Egypt. Set accepted the decision and made peace with Heru. All the gods rejoiced. Thus ends the legend of Asar, Aset, and Heru.

The Resurrection of Asar and his reincarnation in the form of Heru is a symbol for the spiritual resurrection which must occur in the life of every human being. In this manner, the story of the Asarian (Osirian) Trinity of Asar-Aset-Heru and the Egyptian Ennead holds hidden teachings, which when understood and properly practiced, will lead to spiritual enlightenment.

Part IIII
The Mystical Symbolism
of
The Characters in the
Asarian (Osirian) Mystery

The Mystical Symbolism of
The Characters in the Asarian (Osirian) Mystery

The characters in the Asarian (Osirian) Mystery originated in the Mysteries of Anu. Anu is the city where the first major priesthood of the dynastic period arose. Anu was the seat of the worship of Supreme Being in the aspect of a solar divinity. Thus, all forms of the Supreme Being were associated with the Sun as their most visible and powerful symbol. The Pyramid texts of *Pepi II* determine the company of Gods and Goddesses of Anu to be: Tem, Shu, Tefnut, Geb, Nut, Asar (Osiris), Aset (Isis), Set and Nebehet (Nephthys). Of these, Asar (Osiris), Aset (Isis), Set and Nebehet (Nephthys) play a most important role in the Asarian (Osirian) Mystery. Each character in the Asarian (Osirian) Myth is a symbol of the human struggle for spiritual emancipation. Each of them carry a message for the spiritual aspirant which is woven into the fabric of the teaching. It is imparted through the principles which the characters represent and through the interactions between them throughout the story. Therefore, we may proceed now to discover some of the most important mystical implications of the symbols and characters of the Asarian (Osirian) Myth.

Asar (Osiris)
Incarnation of the Higher Self into the realm of time and space

Asar uttered his own name, *Asar,* and thereby brought the world and all life within it into existence. This is the process of Divine incarnation whereby the Supreme Being becomes the universe. Asar (*Lord of the Perfect Black*) is the personification of the blackness of the vast un-manifest regions of existence. Asar is the essence of all things and the very soul of every human being - his/her Higher Self, who, through ignorance, has become involved in the world and is struggling to

Asar

achieve its original state of perfection. Asar symbolizes the fragmented ocean of consciousness which has been cut into pieces by the Lower Self. No longer is there a vast all-encompassing, all-knowing, all-seeing consciousness. The Divine has become limited in association with the human body due to the desire to experience human feelings and egoistic sentiments. Instead of looking at the universe through the cosmic mind, the Divine now expresses himself through billions of life forms whose bodies, minds and senses are too limited to see the vastness of creation.

Set
The lower self

Set represents the unbridled lower self of all human beings. His impulsiveness and reckless passionate pursuits are the ever present enemy of the aspirant or anyone else who is striving for control over the urges of the mind and body. The lower self is represented by the desires of the mind which lure the soul into the varied situations where it experiences pain and pleasure in the world of time and space (the relative existence). These desires lead to selfishness, greed, hatred, anger, lust and other human failings. Set is also identified with the desert, the waste land. This is a symbolic reference to those who are selfish, argumentative and egoistic. Their life is based on fighting with others over what they have not earned and therefore, they live a life which is constantly agitated and devoid of real peace. They are constantly seeking to fulfill their needs and desires and rarely feel contented except temporarily when they are feeling that they are getting what they want. This may be by hook or by crook. They do not think about the feelings of others, only about what they want and they don't care if they must hurt others to get it. This is the *Setian* quality and it is a negative feature in the personality of those who are at a low level of spiritual evolution.

Set

Those who act in an egoistic fashion *destroy* their ability to use reason. Their actions are based on impulse and emotion and they are easily carried away with their desires. Thus, it is Set (egoism, selfishness, desire, greed, hatred, anxiety, lust, etc.) who brings the downfall of Asar.

Aset (Isis)
Love and Wisdom

The motherly love of Aset is instrumental in discovering and putting the pieces of Asar dead body back together. The two most important features which Aset encompasses are love and wisdom. Aset's undying love and devotion to Asar transcended her loss of him twice. This divine devotion led her to discover the pieces of Asar's (Osiris') dead body. This is the devotion of the initiate which leads him or her to the Divine. All that is needed is a deep, ardent love for the Divine.

Aset

The name "ASET" represents wisdom itself which bestows the knowledge of the true Self of the initiate. In the Asarian Mysteries, when Set killed Asar by tearing him into pieces, he was symbolically tearing up the soul. However, Aset restores the pieces of the soul Asar. Therefore, Pride and Insolence (Set-egoism) destroy the soul and Knowledge of the Self (Aset), restores it to its true nature.

Aset is the wisdom faculty within the heart of everyone which can be developed through the practice of the teachings. This kind of wisdom is not intellectual. When you go to school you get intellectual information which you use for a job to live in society but you remain the same personality. The wisdom which Aset represents is the wisdom that comes from actually experiencing the Divine, from being one with the Divine. This wisdom has a transformative effect on the mind. You discover your true identity as not being separate from God but as being one with the Supreme. When Aset imparts this wisdom she is said to be *unveiling* her true nature.

> *"I Aset (Isis), am all that has been, all that is, or shall be; and no mortal man hath ever unveiled me."*

A devotee of ASET (ISIS) is: *One who ponders over sacred matters and seeks therein for hidden truth.* It is not enough to just hear the ancient myths or to understand them at an intellectual level. The aspirant must go deep within him/herself to discover the subtle ideas being conveyed. *Plutarch* describes the character of an initiate of Aset (Isis) as:

> *He alone is a true servant or follower of this Goddess who, after has heard, and has been made acquainted in a proper manner (initiated into the philosophy) with the history of the actions of these gods, searches into the hidden truths which lie concealed under them, and examines the whole by the dictates of reason and philosophy. Nor indeed, ought such an examination to be looked on as unnecessary whilst there are so many ignorant of the true reason even of the most ordinary rites observed by the Egyptian priests, such as their shavings and wearing linen garments. Some, indeed, there are who never trouble themselves to think at all about these matters, whilst others rest satisfied with the most superficial accounts of them. They pay a peculiar veneration to the sheep, therefore they think it their duty not only to abstain from eating flesh, but likewise from wearing its wool. They are continually mourning for their gods, therefore they shave themselves.*

In this manner, Aset is one with Asar and all who come to her temple are given wisdom which leads them to experience the Divine. This wisdom is the intuitional realization which comes from pondering on the nature of the Divine. Pondering implies repeated reflection on the Divine, trying, with sincerity and humility, to understand.

Nebethet (Nephthys)
Nature and Death

Nebehet is the sister of Asar and she represents nature and the natural phase of life called death. Nature is what the spirit impregnates with its life giving essence. Therefore, nature Nebehet is the recipient of Asar's seed (spirit). According to natural law, anything that is born must be subject to the laws of nature and ultimately die. In his original form, detached from nature, Asar was timeless, immortal, and untouched by the passions and frailties of human nature. As an incarnation of the Divine, Asar becomes intoxicated with nature and becomes associated with it through intercourse with Nebehet. This is the predicament of every individual human being. The human spirit becomes involved with nature in the form of the natural elements and thereby produces a physical body composed of an aggregate of physical elements (water, earth, fire, air) which interact in various ways through the qualities of each (review chapter 3 of *Egyptian Yoga: The Philosophy of Enlightenment*).

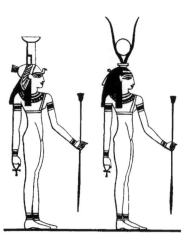

There is deep mystical symbolism in the images and teachings surrounding the Triad or Asar, Aset and Nebehet. In the temples of *Denderah, Edfu and Philae*, there are sculptured representations of the Mysteries of Asar (Osiris). These show *"the* Asar*"* (initiate) lying on a bier and Aset and Nebehet are nearby and are referred to as the "two widows" of the dead

Forms of Nebethet

The Birth of Horus

Asar. In the reliefs of the temples and various papyri, Aset and Nebehet are represented as looking almost exactly alike, the only difference being in their head dress: Aset 𓊽, Nebehet 𓎺 or 𓎱. However, the symbols of these goddesses are in reality just inverted. The symbol of Nebehet is the symbol of Aset when inverted 𓊽➔𓎱. Therefore, each is a reflection of the other and it may be also said that both are aspects of the same principle. This likeness which Aset and Nebehet share is important when they are related to Asar.

Asar sits on the throne and he is supported by the two goddesses, Aset and Nebehet. Symbolically, Asar represents the Supreme Soul, the all-encompassing Divinity which transcends time and space. Aset (Isis) represents wisdom and enlightened consciousness. She is the knower of all words of power and has the power to resurrect Asar and Heru. Nebehet represents temporal consciousness or awareness of time and space. She is related to mortal life and mortal death. This symbolism is evident in the sistrums which bear the likeness of Aset on one side and Nebehet on the other and the writings of Plutarch where he says that Aset represents "generation" while Nebehet represents "chaos and dissolution". Also, in the hiero-

glyphic texts, Aset is referred to as the "day" and Nebehet as the "night". Aset symbolizes the things that "are" and Nebehet represents the things which will "come into being and then die". Thus, enlightenment is being referred to here in the relationship of Asar, Aset and Nebehet and it is this enlightened state of mind which the initiate in the Asarian Mysteries (*Asar Shetaiu*) has as the goal. To become one with Asar means to attain the consciousness of Asar, to become aware of the transcendental, infinite and immortal nature while being aware of the temporal and fleeting human nature.

*Review the section entitled "The teachings of the temple of Aset (Isis) and The Diet of the Initiates" in the book *"Initiation Into Egyptian Yoga: The Secrets of Sheti"*.

Anpu (Anubis)
Discernment and Discrimination

Anpu is the trained intellect of the aspirant. This implies the ability to discipline the body and mind so as to not get caught up in the illusions or emotions of the mind. When the mind and its wavelike thought vibrations are under control, the way is open to spiritual realization in an atmosphere of peace and harmony. This peace and harmony does not necessarily imply an outer situation of calm. It does imply an inward peace which comes from understanding the implications of the wisdom teachings. Anpu represents the dawn when darkness turns to light. He watches over the balance (scales) in the hall of judgment of the *Book of Coming Forth By Day* (See chapter 10 and pages 117, 192) with extreme diligence and in the aspect of *Apuat*, he is the *Opener of the Ways* who leads souls to the *Elysian Fields in the Great Oasis.* Therefore, his great quality of discrimination allows the aspirant to *diligently* watch the mind and to determine which thoughts are divine and which are egoistic and tending towards nature and its perils (life, death, pain, pleasure, etc.). Anpu, as the son of Nebehet and Asar is therefore, a combination of nature (Nebehet) and spiritual aspiration (Asar).

Anpu

As the principle of discriminative intellect, Anpu represents the aspirant who has developed a keen understanding of what is real and what is unreal. This form of reason is the most important quality that needs to be developed by an aspirant who is on the path of spiritual discovery. You must be able to know, at least intellectually, what the world is and is not, what you are and what you are not, etc. The teachings contain many precepts of wisdom but they are not truly real for you until you discover the truths for yourself. However, through your developed intellect you should be able to reason that physical matter is not really solid even though your senses tell you that it is. You should be able to reason that you are in reality an immortal spirit and not just a physical body composed of elements even though you do not yet have experience of your immortality. This reasoning process is the kind of discriminative knowledge which will lead you to self-discovery.

The jackal deity has two aspects, Anpu (Anubis) is the embalmer, the one who prepares the initiate, the *Shti* (one who is in his coffin—the body). Up to this point the initiate is considered to be dead, a mummy, since he/she does not have conscious realization of the transcendental reality beyond the ego-personality. At this stage, the aspirant must be prepared (virtue and physical purification) to receive the teaching because without preparation, the highest teaching would fall on deaf ears. The next aspect is *Apuat, The opener of the Ways*. In this context Anpu represents vigilance and constant practice of discrimination and watchfulness (mindfulness) over the ego-self. Apuat represents the development of intuitional realization

Sebek

which occurs in degrees. Gradually, the ego self becomes effaced and reveals the true Self as one with Amun. Then the mysterious hidden essence of all things is realized as one's very self. All of a sudden it is realized that this was always the true self and that the individual ego personality was a misunderstanding born out of one's ignorance.

Sebek
Sublimated Spiritual Energy

Another deity which symbolizes the idea of the sublimated animal energies in man is the Neter *Sebek (Sbk, Sobk)* 🐊. In alternate versions of the Asarian myth Sebek assists Aset by carrying the body of the dead Asar and protecting it from evil. Sebek is a crocodile god who, like Set, symbolizes the natural forces of nature. In the uncontrolled state, Sebek is a dangerous beast who kills all who cross his path. In this aspect, he is an associate of Set as the one who fetters humans. In the tamed (sublimated) state, Sebek is a formidable ally to Asar in repulsing the forces of evil. In the Pyramid Texts, Sebek assists in the overthrow of Set, and like Anpu, he is made to lead the initiate along the spiritual path and restore the *Eyes* (intuitional vision of the divine) to the deceased (initiate).

Heru (Horus)
Divinity - The Sun Divinity

Heru is the original pre-dynastic form of the Supreme Being associated with the sun. Heru (God) and Het-heru (the house of Heru) were the first divinities to be worshipped generally throughout ancient Egypt and such, were the first theological expression of the duality of existence. The Supreme Being lives within his own house, the universe. Thus, God (spirit) and Goddess (creation) are in reality one and the same. In the pyramid texts, at the beginning of the dy-

Heru

nastic period, the symbol of Heru, ⳼, is used interchangeably with ⌐, The Neter. In dynastic times Heru was associated with Heru as in the Asarian (Osirian) Mystery where he was represented in the form of Heru-p-khart or Heru the child, who later becomes Min, the *avenger of his father*.

Heru Sa Asar Aset
The Rebirth of the Spiritual Life — The Birth of the Spiritual Life

Heru (Horus) is the rebirth of the spirit of the Divine. This rebirth is not a physical birth from the womb, but a rebirth of the mind. No longer is there interest in worldly pursuits which are empty and shallow. Instead, there is a burning desire to conquer the lower self and regain the original glory and freedom of knowing and becoming one with the Higher Self. This is symbolized by Heru regaining the throne of Upper and Lower Egypt. In doing so he has regained mastership of the higher and the lower states of consciousness.

Heru and Set
The Struggle between the Higher Self and the lower self — Purification

The struggle between Heru and Set is the struggle of every human being to control the mind with its erratic desires, longings, unfulfilled expectations and disappointments. This struggle is not avoidable by anyone who is not enlightened. Most people succumb under the weight of the lower self and its desires for fulfillment. This is a pathetic development which those people have allowed to develop due to their own indulgence in the sensual desires of the body and also due to their ignorance of their divine nature which is buried deep within under the egoistic thoughts and unconscious ignorant

feelings. When aspiration arises, the aspirant practices living according to the precepts of Maat until life becomes an expression of virtuous order, leading to the stage of *Maa-keru* or being true of word and deed. This process serves to cleanse the heart (mind) of the impurities of the lower self and place the aspirant on the road to victory. When the light of wisdom and the determination to pursue the divine arise, then struggle becomes a holy war against ignorance and illusion within one's own consciousness. From this struggle arises understanding and strength which leads to final victory of the Higher Self over the lower.

The objective is to sublimate the feelings of anger, hatred, greed, jealousy, and bigotry within oneself. The battle of Heru and Set is a battle within the aspirant to choose where to focus his/her time, energy and emotions. This is proven by the ancient relief of the combination deity Heru-Set where the two are depicted as sharing one body with their two heads.

"Follow your heart throughout your life. Do more than is required of you. Spend no more time on daily cares than required by your household, when wealth ultimately arrives, then too follow your heart for wealth does no good if you are downhearted."

Heru-Set

"Contemplate thy powers, contemplate thy wants and thy connections; so shalt thou discover the duties of life, and be directed in all thy ways."

—Ancient Egyptian Proverbs

After the necessary duties are performed for your sustenance (job, household chores, etc.), what do you do? Do you engage in uplifting endeavors? Are they virtuous? Do they lead to a sense of peace and fulfillment? Do they lead you to activities where there is a lot of aggravation, annoyance and distress? Are you in constant pursuit of satisfying some desire or fancy in your mind? Do you gossip and engage in emotionality or do you feel inclined to go to a quiet place and study the teachings? Do you refrain from engaging in fits of anger and hurtful comments toward others or do you enjoy picking fights or watching others hurt each other?

Wherever you direct your mind, there you will be. If you direct it to activities which involve a lot of extrovertedness, argumentativeness and unrest, you will have that kind of mind even when there is peace and quiet. However, if you direct the mind to peace and harmony, in time, you will have peace and harmony even under the most stressful conditions. This is the miracle and mystery of the mind. Where the attention goes, the energy and desire flows as well. Thus, the challenge for a spiritual aspirant is to lead him/herself to become more *Heruian* instead of *Setian*. The path of Heru, virtue, heroism and effacement of the ego, leads to spiritual enlightenment and victory while the path of Set, ignorance and egoism, leads to an endless search for fulfillment of worldly desires. The path of Set is the cycle of birth and death and countless experiences of disappointments and unfulfilled desires. Thus if you have fanciful notions of being happy in the world of human experience you are living life based on illusion and ignorance because no one is truly happy in the world. If you choose to live according to the precepts of Maat, then you are aligning yourself with order, truth and reality.

Djehuti

Above: Horus, son of Osiris and Isis.

Osiris in the character of Menu, the "god of the uplifted arm," and Harpokrates as they sat in the disk of the moon, from the third day of the new moon until the fifteenth day. Below is the Crocodile-god Sebek bearing the mummy of the god on his back. To the left stands Isis.

From a bas-relief at Philae.

Djehuti (Tehuti, Thoth)
Reason

The struggle between Heru and Set does not end with either destroying the other. Heru pursues the path of reason seeking counsel with the wisdom of Djehuti and Aset. Set, the lower self, refuses to abide by the decree of wisdom but he is eventually sublimated through his own humiliation and ignorance. In the end, when the aspirant is aligned with all divine forces, the lower self can no longer struggle. The overwhelming force of the Divine pushes the lower self into a position of service rather than of mastership. This is symbolized by the relief which shows Set protecting the Barque of Ra from the evil serpent Apep (Apophis).

Thus, Djehuti represents the reasoning aspect of the mind (intellect) when it is aligned with the Higher Self (God). Djehuti is the intuitional quality of the mind which can receive the wisdom from the spirit because it is not tainted by ignorance or egoism.

The god Djehuti in the ritual act (movement) of stretching the cloth.
Karnak Temple 18th Dynasty, Egypt, Africa

The King handing the Djed Pillar (of Asar) to Aset
(from a bas relief at the temple of Asar at Abdu (Abydos).

Part ||||||
Healthy Life Style, Diet and Nutrition, Preventative Health and Daily Yoga Practices

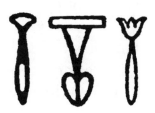

THE DIET OF THE GENERAL ANCIENT EGYPTIAN POPULATION AND THE MEDICAL SYSTEM

Hippocrates (460?-377? BCE), who has been called the *father of medicine* and whose major teaching was that diet is the cause of disease, was instructed in this most important health factor by the physicians of ancient Egypt. Herodotus witnessed an elaborate system of medical science during his travels in Egypt. The following is an excerpt from his writings where he notes the general dietary practices of the ancient Egyptian people.

> The Egyptians who live in the cultivated parts of the country, by their practice of keeping records of the past, have made themselves much the best historians of any nation of which I have experience. I will describe some of their habits:
>
> 1. Every month for three consecutive days they purge themselves, for their health's sake, with emetics* and clysters, in the belief that all diseases come from the food a man eats; and it is a fact - even apart from this precaution - that next to the Libyans they are the healthiest people in the world.
>
> 2. I should put this down myself to the absence of changes in the climate, for change, and especially changes of weather, is the prime cause of disease.
>
> 3. They eat loaves of Spelt - *cyllestes* is their word for them...
>
> 4....and drink a wine made from barley, as they have no vines in the country.

5. Some kinds of fish they eat raw, either dried in the sun, or salted; quails, too, they eat raw, and ducks and various small birds, after pickling them in brine; other sorts of birds and fish, apart from those which are considered sacred, they either roast or boil.

6...nevertheless they are peculiar in certain ways which they have discovered of living more cheaply: for instance, they gather the water-lilies (Lotuses) which grow in great abundance when the river is full and floods the neighboring flats, and dry them in the sun; then from the center of each blossom they pick out something which resembles a poppyhead, grind it, and make it into loaves which they bake. The root of this plant is also edible; it is round, about as big as an apple, and tastes sweet.

7. There is another kind of lily to be found in the river; this resembles a rose, and its fruit is formed on a separate stalk from that which bears the blossom, and has very much the looks of a wasp's comb. The fruit contains a number of seeds, about the size of an olive-stone, which are good to eat either green or dried.

8. They pull up the annual crop of papyrus-reed which grows in the mashes, cut the stalks in two, and eat the lower part, about eighteen inches in length, first baking it in a closed pan, heated red-hot, if they want to enjoy it to perfection. The upper section of the stalk is used for some other purpose.

9. Some of these people, however, live upon nothing but fish, which they gut as soon as they catch them, and eat after drying them in the sun.

*An *emetic* is any medicinal agent used to induce vomiting. In India, Yogis practice a similar procedure for cleansing the upper gastrointestinal tract. It is called *Jala Dhauti.* The procedure is to ingest 4-5 glasses of lukewarm water with a small amount of salt in it, then shake up the intestines through massaging and abdominal movements and then vomit the water out using the fingers. This has the effect of removing phlegm and bile.

A- Another important point is that the sun was used for much of the cooking as opposed to stoves, and even worse, microwave ovens which destroy both the gross and subtle nutritional quality of foods.

B- Many foods were eaten raw and vegetables made up a major part of the diet.

C- Wheat was not a major part of the diet. Spelt was used instead. In Indian Ayur-Veda science, wheat has been found to be incompatible with some people, causing them phlegm or congestion.

D- The ancient Egyptians lived in an area of the world where the climate was stable. This is important because their physical bodies were not subjected to drastic changes such as in those areas where seasonal temperature changes range many degrees. There are certain locations in the world where the climates change many degrees within a single day. This occurrence is jolting to the body's equilibrium and thus affects general health. This factor of the geographical climate became a primary teaching of Jesus in the Essene Gospel of Peace. Also, this Gospel describes cooking with the sun as well as the proper methods of food combining, attitude when eating and methods of internal cleansing through fasts and enemas.

THE TEACHINGS OF THE TEMPLE OF ASET (ISIS) AND THE DIET OF THE INITIATES

While the general population was considered to be one of the most healthy groups of the ancient world, the spiritual initiates were required to keep even more strict dietary practices. The special diets of the ancient Egyptian initiates were a highly guarded secret as were the inner meanings of the myths which were acted out in the mystery rituals (**SHETAUT NETER**). For this reason, many of the special yogic practices which included a special diet and meditation were not committed to writing in an explicit fashion. Rather, they were committed to hieroglyphic form and carried on through the initiatic process. It was not until Greek historians and initiates into the Egyptian mystery schools began to write about their experiences that the more detailed aspects of the initiatic diets were available to a wider audience. The sect of Jews called the Essenes practiced an initiation period of two to three years and instituted purification diets and hygienic practices similar to those spoken about by Herodotus (484?-425 BCE) and Plutarch (46?-120 ACE). The Essenic health practices were presented in the Essene Gospel of Peace.

The Three Kinds of Foods and The Three Classes of Foods

Every human being needs three kinds of foods in order to survive and thrive. First, the body and nervous system need physical food to sustain the body. Clearly the ideal here is a vegetarian diet composed of fresh vegetables and fruits. Secondly, the human personality needs mental food. This means nurturing, love and compassion, which comes from loved ones, to feed the emotional needs; and then at a higher level, wisdom teachings and spiritual aspiration to enlighten the mind, which comes from good association with higher minded people, the spiritual preceptor in particular. This is food for thought. Then the personality needs food for the soul. This comes through meditation and transcendence of the lower nature. This is self-discovery. Those deprived from any of these will suffer anxiety and frustration in life.

The Ancient Egyptian Texts state that one cannot expect to obtain results unless one is:

"mentally pure and physically pure."

These are the keys to accomplishing any goal in life and, enlightenment is a goal like any other, albeit the highest goal. With respect to attaining the goal of enlightenment, all other goals are like dust blowing in the wind. The following instruction will serve as guidelines for meditation and is not intended to be a substitute for a competent instructor. There are many techniques of meditation. Here we will focus on basic techniques of "moving" meditations for initially calming the mind of the beginning practitioner.

Another important factor of meditation is that health of the body must be maintained through proper diet and proper exercise. This means that the diet should be composed of fresh whole foods and it should be exclusively vegetarian. You cannot expect to have success in meditation if you have a weak constitution or if your are constantly craving foods which heighten the body consciousness and negative emotions (meats) or those which have drug-like effects on the body (sugars). The mind is affected by these in the same manner that it is affected by other mind altering drugs. Therefore, a spiritual aspirant must cleanse the mind and body in order to climb the ladder of spiritual evolution.

Many people do not realize that what they consume has a strong effect on their psyche. This implies not only foods but all manner of consumption. Just as there are three major states of relative consciousness, there are three basic kinds of foods. The first group is composed of those foods which engender restlessness, agitation and distraction.

Ex. sugars, salty foods, dry foods, hot spices, coffee, fish, poultry, eggs, etc.

These foods promote passion, stimulate the emotions and excite the body. Also eating in a hurry promotes restlessness and distraction. The second group is composed of foods which promote dullness. This group includes:

meats, tobacco, alcohol, fermented foods, processed foods, stale or overripe foods.

These foods promote dullness of intellect, anger, hatred, greed, volatility, negative thoughts, disease and clouded reasoning ability. These foods are filled with negativity due to the way in which they are handled in the food processing system. The addition of unnatural chemicals to food in and of itself is reason enough to classify them as tainted with poison. The killing of animals effectively poisons the food with negative hormones as well as fear vibrations from the animals. Also the human digestive tract is not designed to handle meat so the food rots as it passes through the intestinal system, causing diseases such as cancer. Is there any wonder why medical doctors admonish those who contract cancer or experience heart trouble to stop eating meat and to stop smoking? Shouldn't they begin promoting a meat free diet for everyone (including themselves) at an early age? If smoking is known to produce cancer shouldn't it be outlawed as are other addictive drugs? Poisons are sold out of greed and ignorance. Also, such poisons are consumed due to ignorance and addictive desire.

Dull foods are not good for the body or for the mind, but much like the stimulating foods, they create an addictive form of dependency wherein even when the person has a full understanding of the deleterious effects of the foods, he or she continues to consume them anyway using the excuse "well I want to enjoy my life even if I shorten it". The weakened will disables a person's reasoning capacity as well as their willpower to resist the urge for the foods.

Lucid foods are those which promote harmony, inner mental peace, bright intellect, willpower, etc. They foster purity of the mind as well as the body. They are nutritious and enhance the body's ability to fight off disease. Lucid foods include:

whole foods, cereals, fresh vegetables and fruits, legumes, seeds, nuts, sprouted seeds, herb teas, honey.

A serious spiritual aspirant must learn about the nature of food as he or she climbs the ladder of mystical spirituality. In so doing, a healthy constitution can be created which will allow for a positive and fruitful spiritual movement towards self-discovery. Since every human being is

not exactly the same as another, the exact diet which is optimal for each individual will be slightly different. Therefore each individual should experiment with their diet within the broad guidelines given above in order to discover the right combination within the Lucid Diet category which is best suited for him or her.

Plutarch, a student of the mysteries of Aset, reported that the initiates followed a strict diet made up of vegetables and fruits and *abstained from particular kinds of foods* (swine, sheep, fish, etc.) *as well as indulgence of the carnal appetite.* In the following excerpts Plutarch describes the purpose and procedure of the diet observed by the Initiates of Aset and the goal to be attained through the rigorous spiritual program. This next excerpt should be studied carefully.

To desire, therefore, and covet after truth, those truths more especially which concern the divine nature, is to aspire to be partakers of that nature itself (1), and to profess that all our studies (2) and inquiries (2) are devoted to the acquisition of holiness. This occupation is surely more truly religious than any external (3) purifications or mere service of the temple can be. (4) But more especially must such a disposition of mind be highly acceptable to that goddess to whose service you are dedicated, for her special characteristics are wisdom and foresight, and her very name seems to express the peculiar relation which she bears to knowledge. For "Aset (Isis)" is a Greek word, and means "knowledge or wisdom,"(5) and "Typhon," [Set] the name of her professed adversary, is also a Greek word, and means " pride and insolence."(6) This latter name is well adapted to one who, full of ignorance and error, tears in pieces (7) and conceals that holy doctrine (about Asar (Osiris)) which the goddess collects, compiles, and delivers to those who aspire after the most perfect participation in the divine nature. This doctrine inculcates a steady perseverance in one uniform and temperate course of life (8), and an abstinence

from particular kinds of foods (9), as well as from all indulgence of the carnal appetite (10), and it restrains the intemperate and voluptuous part within due bounds, and at the same time habituates her votaries to undergo those austere and rigid ceremonies which their religion obliges them to observe. The end and aim of all these toils and labors is the attainment of the knowledge of the First and Chief Being (11), who alone is the object of the understanding of the mind; and this knowledge the goddess invites us to seek after, as being near and dwelling continually (12) with her. And this also is what the very name of her temple promiseth to us, that is to say, the knowledge and understanding of the eternal and self-existent Being - now it is called "Iseion," which suggests that if we approach the temple of the goddess rightly, we shall obtain the knowledge of that eternal and self-existent Being.

Mystical Implications of the Discourse of Plutarch:*

*Note: The numbers at the beginning of each paragraph below correspond to the reference numbers in the text above.

1- It is to be understood that spiritual aspiration implies seeking the union with or becoming one with the thing being sought because this is the only way to truly "know" something. You can have opinions about what it is like to be a whale but you would never exactly know until you become one with it. God enfolding all that exists is the one being worthy of veneration and identification. This "knowing" of Neter (God) is the goal of all spiritual practices. This is the supreme goal which must be kept in mind by a spiritual aspirant.

2- In order to discover the hidden nature of God, emphasis is placed on study and inquiry into the nature of things. Who am I? What is the universe composed of? Who is God? How am I related to God? These are the questions which when pursued, lead to the discovery of the Self (God). Those who do not engage in this form of inquiry

will generate a reality for themselves according to their beliefs. Some people believe they have the answers, that the universe is atoms and electrons or energy. Others believe that the body is the soul and that there is nothing else. Still others believe that the mind is the Soul or that there is no soul and no God. The first qualification for serious aspiration is that you have a serious conviction that you are greater than just a finite individual mortal body, that you are an immortal being who is somehow mixed up with a temporal form (body). If this conviction is present, then you are stepping on the road to enlightenment. The teachings will be useful to you. Those who hold other beliefs are being led by ignorance and lack of spiritual sensitivity as a result of their beliefs. Thus, their beliefs will create a reality for them based on those beliefs. They will need to travel the road of nature which will guide them in time toward the path of spiritual aspiration.

3-4 The plan prescribed by the teachings of yoga is the only true means to effective spiritual development because it reveals the inner meanings of the teachings and it is experiential, i.e. it is based on your own personal experience and not conjecture. Otherwise, worship and religious practices remain at the level of ritualism only and do not lead to enlightenment.

5-7 The name "ASET (ISIS)" represents "wisdom" itself which bestows the knowledge of the true Self of the initiate. In the Asarian (Osirian) Mysteries, when Set killed Asar (Osiris) by tearing him into pieces, he was symbolically tearing up the soul. However, Aset restores the pieces of the soul (Asar). Therefore, Pride and Insolence (Set-egoism) destroy the soul and Knowledge of the Self (Aset) restores it to its true nature. The Greek name for Aset (Isis) is supported by the ancient Egyptian scriptures. One of the names of Aset (Isis) is: *Rekhit* ⬭△⊜◗𓁐 meaning "knowledge personified" and "Aset (Isis)-Sothis". Rekhit is also a name of the God in the "Duat" or Netherworld who possesses knowledge which can lead the soul to the abode of the Divine, thus avoiding the fiends and demoniac personalities of the **Duat** which lead the soul to experience hellish conditions after death. The variation, *Rekh-t* ⬭◦⊕⏤◊⚱, means Sage or learned person.

8- True spirituality cannot be pursued rashly or in a fanatical way by going to extremes. Yoga spirituality is a science of balance. It has been developed over a period of thousands of years with well established principles, which when followed, produce the desired effect of leading the initiate from darkness to light, ignorance to knowledge, an un-enlightened state to enlightenment.

9-10 The foods referred to are flesh foods (swine, sheep, fish, etc.), pulse, and salt. Indulgence in sexual activity has two relevant aspects. First, it intensifies the physical experience of embodiment and distracts the mind by creating impressions in the subconscious which will produce future cravings and desires. This state of mind renders the individual incapable of concentration on significant worldly or high spiritual achievements. Secondly, control of the sexual urge leads to control of the sexual Life Force energy, which can then be directed toward higher mental and spiritual achievement.

11- See #1.

12- There are two very important points in this line. Once again we are being reminded that good association or keeping the company of sages or other enlightened personalities is a powerful means to gain knowledge of the state of enlightenment. To this end, strive to keep good company in your family relations as well as non-family relations. Read uplifting books by the sages and the teachings of the masters. When you discover a more evolved personality, seek to maintain contact by reading their teachings and through correspondence. Do not debate with those who lack spiritual sensitivity. This form of interaction will weaken your mind. As Jesus said: *Cast not your pearls before swine, for they will trample them as they turn*

against you. Trust in the Omniscient Divine Self, who knows past, present and future, who manifests as Nature to lead others on the path. Spread the teachings of yoga to those who are interested only or with those whom you practice. This kind of interaction will help you both to increase your understanding and generate a positive frame of mind.

The second important point here refers to continuous reflection and meditation on the divine which is also expressed in the opening prayer in page one of this book: *"Give thyself to GOD, keep thou thyself daily for God; and let tomorrow be as today."* It implies that one's mind should be constantly remembering the divine and glorifying the divine in all things. It means not allowing the mind to develop attachments to the fleeting events of human life be they positive experiences or negative ones. It means not allowing the negative thoughts and feelings to lead you into a pursuit of illusory pleasures of the senses which will draw you away from divine awareness and realization. It means centering the mind on self discovery and introspection at all times regardless of what your activities may be and those activities should be based solely on the principles of virtue, justice and order. This form of spiritual practice is known as "mindfulness" in Buddhism and Vedanta Philosophies.

Plutarch further reports that the Egyptian initiates:

> *...strive to prevent fatness in Apis† as well as themselves(1), for they are anxious that their bodies should sit as light and easy about their souls as possible, and that their mortal part* (body) *should not oppress and weigh down their divine and immortal part...during their more solemn purifications they abstain from wine* (2) *wholly, and they give themselves up entirely to study* (4) *and meditation(5) and to the hearing* (3) *and teaching of these divine truths which teach of the divine na-*

ture. † Bull which was kept as a symbol of Asar (Osiris) and Ptah.

The following dietary guidelines for spiritual and physical health are derived from the above statement.

1- Preventing "fatness"- obesity. This issue is very important even for those without spiritual aspirations. Some people who are overweight claim that they are happy and content as they are. Some scientists claim to have discovered a gene in the human system which causes a propensity to become overweight. Once again, all of your body's characteristics are due to your past karmic history of experiences and desires, not only in this lifetime but in previous ones as well. Physical weight is like a physical object which is possessed. The more you have, the more you try to hold onto, and the more stress you have trying to enjoy and hold onto "things". Desires of the body such as eating have a grounding effect on the soul because they engender the desire to experience the physical pleasure of consuming food. Desires of the body as well as strong emotions such as hate, greed, etc., have the effect of rendering the mind insensitive to spirituality. Excess weight on the body causes innumerable health problems to arise.

You can change the future condition of your body by first mentally resolving to change it and then employing the self-effort in that direction while at the same time invoking the help of the Neters (cosmic forces - divine energies of God) to assist your quest for self-improvement. This will not be easy since the temptation of food is very great. It is related to the first energy center of the subtle spiritual body (Uraeus-Kundalini Serpent Power)* and it is a force which needs to be controlled in order to proceed on the spiritual path. As part of your spiritual program, begin controlling your intake of food gradually, on a daily basis. Even if you cut back a tablespoonful per

day until you reach a level of intake which will support the normal weight for your body structure. Be especially watchful of yourself in respect to your habits. Do you eat out of habit, for pleasure or out of necessity? If it is out of habit or for pleasure, you must break the cycle by engaging in other activities when the desire arises. Do exercise, deep breathing, study, chant, call a fellow practitioner for support. The Serpent power will be discussed in detail in two future sections. *see audio tape lecture KUNDALINI - URAEUS YOGA: Workshop and Cleansing Meditation - I.

2- Natural wines and other naturally brewed drinks may be acceptable in general society for the masses in small quantities, but not for the serious student of yoga (initiate, aspirant). You will notice that as you purify yourself, you will not be able to tolerate even a small amount of intoxicants. Distilled liquor is not a natural substance. It is processed into a potent form which is injurious to the body and is therefore, not suitable at all for use by those advancing on the spiritual path. The same applies to narcotics and all other "recreational" drugs. All of these distort the spiritual perception while damaging the physical body. No drug can produce a high which can be compared to spiritual bliss. Therefore, resolve to leave all drugs behind and become intoxicated with spiritual feelings and aspiration.

3,4,5- Once again, the main format for spiritual education is:

3- Listening to the teachings.‡
4- Constant study and reflection on the teachings.‡
5- Meditation on the meaning of the teachings.‡

‡Note: It is important to note here that the same teaching which was practiced in Ancient Egypt of **Listening** to, **Reflecting** upon, and **Meditating** upon the teachings is the same process used in Vedanta-Jnana Yoga of today.

Chapter 30B of the *Book of Coming Forth By Day* states:

> *This utterance (hekau) shall be recited by a person purified and washed; one who has not eaten animal flesh or fish.*

Chapter 137A of the *Book of Coming Forth By Day* states:

> *And behold, these things shall be performed by one who is clean, and is ceremonially pure, a man who hath eaten neither meat nor fish, and who hath not had intercourse with women.* * (applies to female initiates not having intercourse with men as well)

In the Mysteries of Asar and Aset, Set represents the lower human nature and Heru the Higher. Set kills Asar and usurps the throne which rightfully should belong to Heru, Asar's son. In various renderings of the characteristics of Set, it is stated that Set is promiscuous. Most interestingly, both Heru and Set are vegetarians. Their favorite food is *lettuce*. Therefore, we are to understand that vegetarianism increases the potential for spiritual advancement and for the vital sexual force. With this understanding, it is clear that control of the sexual urge to conserve potential spiritual energy and purification of the diet are necessary practices on the spiritual path which enable the aspirant to achieve increased spiritual sensitivity. When practiced correctly, the conserved energy can be transformed into spiritual energy by directing it through the various energy centers in the body until it finally reaches the center of intuitional vision (Eye of Heru-Udjat).

A most important point to remember when beginning practices for the purification of the body is that they should be implemented gradually, preferably under the supervision of an experienced person. If these changes result in an inability to perform your daily duties, then they are too extreme. The key to advancement in any area

is steady, balanced practice. There must always be a balance between the practical life and the spiritual. In this way, spiritual advancement occurs in an integral fashion, intensifying every area of one's life rather than one particular area exclusively. All areas must be mastered, secular as well as non-secular, in order to transcend the world process (illusion of time and space and the ego-self).

Since the physical body and all worldly attainments are changeable, fleeting and ultimately perishable, it would be wise to pursue a way of life which directs the mind toward understanding the Self and not to pursue health as an end in itself, but as a means to your own growth and spiritual evolution, which will continue even after the death of your physical body if you have not attained enlightenment up to the time of physical death. The holistic development of an individual must be directed to achieving a state of consciousness which is not dependent on the physical body for peace and comfort. The body is an instrument which you have created through your thoughts to allow you to pursue the goal of enlightenment and thereby experience the fullness of life.

For more details on the subject of diet, fasting and nutrition see the new book *The Kemetic Diet: Food For Body, Mind and Soul* by Muata Ashby

Left: The goddess Maat (right) and the God Djehuti preside over the scales of karmic fate which judge every human heart. The Ammit monster divides the scale between the third and the fourth sphere of psycho-spiritual consciousness-the Serpent Power.

The Daily Schedule for Yoga Practice

A practitioner of Yoga must be able to integrate the main practices of yoga into daily life. This means that you need to begin adding small amounts of time for Prayer, Repetition of the Divine Name (Hekau), Exercise (includes proper breathing exercise), Study of the Teachings, Silence, Selfless Service, Meditation, and Daily Reflection. This also means that you will gradually reduce the practices which go against yogic movement as you gain more time for Sheti.

Below you will find an outline of a schedule for the beginning practice of Yoga. The times given here are a suggested minimum time for beginners. You may spend more time according to your capacity and personal situation, however, try to be consistent in the amount of time and location you choose to practice your discipline as well as in the time of day you choose to perform each of the different practices. This will enable your body and mind to develop a rhythm which will develop into the driving force of your day. When this occurs you will develop stamina and fortitude when dealing with any situation of life. You will have a stable center which will anchor you to a higher purpose in life whether you are experiencing prosperous times or adverse times. In the advanced stages, spiritual practice will become continuous. Try to do the best you can according to your capacity, meaning your circumstances. If your family members are not interested or do not understand what you are trying to do simply maintain your practices privately and try to keep the interruptions to a minimum. As you develop, you may feel drawn toward some forms of practice over others. The important thing to remember is to practice them all in an integrated fashion. Do not neglect any of the practices even though you may spend additional time on some versus others.

Practicing spirituality only during times of adversity is the mistake of those who are spiritually immature. Any form of spiritual

practice, ritualistic or otherwise is a positive development, however, you will not derive the optimal spiritual benefits by simply becoming religious when you are in trouble. The masses of people only pray when they are in trouble...then they ask for assistance to get out of trouble. What they do not realize is that if they were to turn their minds to God at all times, not just in times of misfortune, adversity would not befall them. As you progress through your studies you will learn that adversities in life are meant to turn you toward the Divine. In this sense they are messages from the Divine to awaken spiritual aspiration. However, if you do not listen to the message and hearken to the Divine intent behind it, you will be in a position to experience more miseries of life and miseries of a more intense nature.

Basic Schedule of Spiritual Practice

1a- Deep breathing, using the *proper breathing technique.*
1b-Alternate Breathing exercise (10 minutes in Am and in PM),
2-Prayer (10-30 minutes in Am* and in PM),

Opening Prayer:

*O Åmen, O Åmen, who art in heaven, turn thy face upon
the dead body of the child, and make your child sound
and strong in the Underworld.*

*O Åmen, O Åmen, O God, O God, O Åmen, I adore thy
name, grant thou to me that I may understand thee;
Grant thou that I may have peace in the Duat, and that
I may possess all my members therein...*

*Hail, Åmen, let me make supplication unto thee, for I
know thy name, and thy transformations are in my
mouth, and thy skin is before my eyes. Come, I pray*

*thee, and place thou thine heir and thine image, myself,
in the everlasting underworld... let my whole body become like that of a neter, let me escape from the evil
chamber and let me not be imprisoned therein; for I
worship thy name..*

3-Exercise (10 minutes in am and before study time),

4-Repetition of the Divine Name in the form of your chosen hekau-
mantra (10 minutes in am and in PM),
5-Meditation practice (10 minutes in Am, should be practiced after
exercise, prayer and repetition of the Divine Name),

Closing Prayer after meditation or any spiritual practice:

*I am pure. I am pure. I am Pure.
I have washed my front parts with the waters of libations, I
have cleansed my hinder parts with drugs which make wholly
clean, and my inward parts have been washed in the liquor of
Maat.*

6-Study of the teachings (reading 30 minutes per day),
7-Silence time (30 minutes per day),
8-Listening to the teachings: Choose an audio recording of a yogic
spiritual preceptor and listen for a minimum of 30 minutes per day
without any distractions if possible. If possible, go to a yogic spiritual center (Ashram, Wat, Temple) where teachings are presented by
a qualified teacher of yoga wisdom. If this is not possible, form a
study group wherein the teachings may be discussed and explored.

9-Selfless service (as required whenever the opportunity presents itself),
10-Daily reflection: Remembering the teachings during the ordinary

course of the day and applying them in daily living situations- to be practiced as much as possible.

*(see Morning Worship and Meditation tape)

The suggested times given above are the minimum amount you should spend on daily spiritual practices each day. Whenever possible you should increase the times according to your capacity and ability. You should train your mind so that it rejoices in hearing about and practicing the teachings of yoga instead of the useless worldly activities. Follow this path gradually but steadily.

Once you have established a schedule of minimal time to devote to practices, even if you do 5-10 minutes of meditation time per day and nothing else, keep your schedule if at all possible. Many people feel that they do not have the time to incorporate even ordinary activities into their lives. They feel overwhelmed with life and feel they have no control. If there is no control it is because there is no discipline. If you make a schedule for all of your activities (spiritual and non-spiritual) and keep to it tenaciously, you will discover that you can control your time and your life. As you discover the glory of spiritual practice, you will find even more time to expand your spiritual program. Ultimately, you will create a lifestyle which is entirely spiritualized. This means that every act in your life will be based on the wisdom teachings (MAAT) and therefore you will not only spend a particular time of day devoted to spiritual practices, but every facet of your life will become a spontaneous worship of the divine.

Please observe the following rules for practicing Yoga exercises.

Exercise and Meditation should be done on an empty stomach.
To increase the intensity of the workout increase the number of repetitions of the exercises according to your capacity.
To increase the meditative aspect of the workout, do less repetitions and hold the postures for a longer period of time.
No undue force should be exerted to get into any of the postures.
You should use a proper mat to avoid slipping and to cushion the spine while performing the exercises.

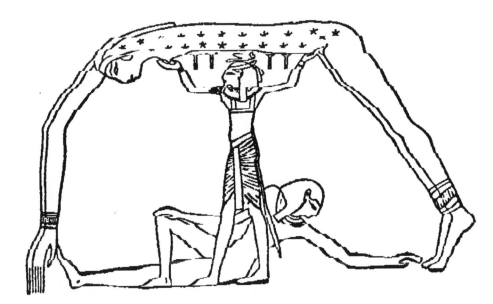

The Separation of Geb and Nut by Shu

Health is the daughter of exercise. This is an Ancient Egyptian proverb of course. But the exercise of the gods and goddesses begins much earlier than the proverbs and is rooted in the hearth of Egyptian mythology. As you have seen in the previous sections, there is a profound mythological teaching within the Asarian (Osirian) Myth. The characters within it portray specific metaphorical ideas and cosmic principles which when understood correctly, can allow the students of mythology and spirituality to discover the hidden truth within their own hearts. Throughout Egyptian writings, reliefs, and steles, there are to be found specific depictions of the characters in the Asarian religious myth which correspond exactly to positions or postures which are today known as *Yoga Postures*. As mentioned earlier, these postures are special, unlike ordinary exercises or positions in which the physical body may be placed, because they are specially designed to have an effect on the psycho-spiritual energy centers of the spiritual (astral) body.

Yoga is not only a discipline of the body. It is an integrated lifestyle which leads to physical, mental and spiritual health. You should not look on yoga only as a means for exercise or as just a means to relax the mind, although the benefits in these areas are well documented, but you should also understand that the greatest success in yoga comes when you adopt it as a lifestyle. You must live it, and then you will discover its deepest secrets.

So let us begin!

Part ||||||
The Exercises,
Yoga Postures
and
Meditations
of
Egyptian Yoga

The Special Features
of the Tjef Neteru System

The Tjef Neteru

Why is the Tjef Neteru Sema Paut Neteru System of Postures and Movements so Unique?

Yoga philosophy recognizes four main aspects of the personality that need to be harmonized and cultivated in order to effect the positive spiritual evolution in a human being. These aspects of the personality include the physical and ethical nature, the emotions, the intellect and the will. The discipline of the postures promotes the positive development of all of the basic aspects of the human personality and is therefore to be considered as an *integral* discipline for promoting spiritual evolution.

The Integral Path

In the yogic field, one can concentrate on a particular aspect of the personality and attain a higher level of spiritual culture. However, in this mode of practice there is a danger of becoming imbalanced in the movement towards spiritual evolution. Many practitioners have become too obsessed with an aspect at the neglect of others. This may lead to some progress in that particular area but also causes a deficiency in the personality due to stagnation in the other areas, which weakens the overall personality and thwarts the personality's ability to cope with and transcend worldly situations. Further, the defect in the personality renders it dull. So one may become intellectually evolved but be emotionally crippled or emotionally expanded but with misunderstanding (blind faith) for example. So the sages have enjoined that an integral movement is more effective in the long run as opposed to a fanatical or imbalanced practice. Spiritual evolution is like growing a fruit tree. It takes its time to bear fruit but providing sun, rain and nutritious soil for it to grow in can shorten the time to its earliest natural and safe possible completion. Unorthodox or obsessive means will eventually frustrate the authentic spiritual movement. So the Ancient Egyptian philosophy and discipline of the movements of the gods and goddesses promotes a balanced and powerful advancement in the spiritual culture.

The Tjef Neteru

Aspect of Personality Affected	Yogic Aspect Promoted in the System
Physical body-Ethical Nature	**Right Action** - Physical movement promote health and balance of subtle energies through posture. Acting like the gods and goddesses is the highest form of action.
Emotions	**Devotion** – opening of the caring feeling towards the higher self through emulation of the Divinities. Developing love for the divinities promotes universal love and is therefore to be considered as a higher form of love than ordinary human relationships, which are limited and finite.
Intellect	**Wisdom movement** – through deepening knowledge of the Divinities, their higher nature as expressions of the inner self and their relationship to higher consciousness. Achieving the knowledge of the divinities is actually a movement for learning about self since these are actually emanations of the innermost reality within oneself.
Will – Unconscious	**Meditative movement** – concentration and absorption of the mind and body with the divine principle through one-pointed identification with the divine principles. The discipline of the postures is for more than just developing physical health. It can lead one to the highest spiritual realization since it harmonizes the physical, mental and emotional natures so that it will become possible to experience a concentration leading to immersion in the essential nature of the innermost reality behind the physical manifestations of the cosmic energies as symbolized

Integral (Wholistic) Yoga

The process of personality Integration.

Love-Contentment ⇔ Understanding ⇔ Peace ⇔ Fulfillment

The Paths of Yoga

Love Contentment	Understanding	Peace	Fulfillment
⬆	⬆	⬆	⬆
Emotion	**Reason**	**Action**	**Will**
⬆	⬆	⬆	⬆
Yoga of Devotional Love	**Yoga of Wisdom**	**Yoga of Righteousness Virtue**	**Yoga of Meditation**
Control of feeling. Directed towards the Divine	Understanding the Divine, Mystical Psychology	Self-control Selfless service. Purity of Heart.	Study of Mind and development of inner powers.

THE INTEGRAL PATH AND MYSTICAL RELIGION

Many practitioners of yoga exercises, especially those who practice the eastern forms, have not understood that it is actually supposed to be a system of physical culture designed for the purpose leading the body to health but also to mental concentration and into a meditative state. The Integral path slide (previous page) shows how the *Tjef neteru Sema Paut Neteru* system of postures works to promote an integral movement in the spiritual practice. Each element in the posture system integrates the four basic yogic elements. This practice is engendered through the systems concept and its spiritual basis which is grounded in the Kemetic (Ancient Egyptian Mythic scheme). The language of myth, especially that of Ancient Egypt, evokes an primordial but familiar way of looking at Creation and our place in it. So our practice is not just physical but also mythological. The study of Kemetic myth (basis of the Tjef neteru) leads us to Devotion and Wisdom since we learn about the divinities and develop feeling for them and then become wise through understanding and experiencing their passion. Following their passion and wisdom leads us to righteous action, living and thinking. As we delve deeper into their mythic origins we are led to their mystical innermost nature as we become meditation in motion and find ourselves not just acting like them but becoming like them or more precisely one of them. Even further, we begin to realize that they are not entities separate from us but rather emanations, as if products of our own will. As the rays are to the sun, we are the very source from which they arise and have their existence. We become aware that we are one and alone, the source of all sources, the ultimate Neter who moves not and yet moves all! This is the vital mystical movement which all human beings long for.

The complete practice of mystical religion incorporates three steps, *Myth, Ritual* and *Metaphysics (i.e. Mysticism)*. These also form an integral part of the *Tjef neteru Sema Paut Neteru* system. Thus, the *Tjef neteru Sema Paut Neteru* system incorporates the following elements:

1. **Myth** – based on the Kamitic tradition
2. **Ritual** – ritual movements emulating the divinities (temple practice).
    a. Physical Culture – promotes physical health and the balancing of the Life Forces as well as the awakening of the Serpent Power.
3. **Mysticism** – promotes a balanced movement of union of the individual personality with its cosmic source by discovering and uniting the

The System of Phases in the Practice of The Egyptian Yoga Postures

The Program of Thef Neteru Yoga differs from other forms of exercise (sports, recreation, games) in several important ways. First, it is a system for developing not only the physical aspect of a human being but also the mental and spiritual aspects as well. This occurs in the following way.

The practice of the physical postures of yoga affect not only the muscles (as ordinary exercises do) but also the nerves and the mind and thus develops the inner Life Force and Serpent Power energies, thereby awakening and cultivating the psychic energies of the Astral Body and the higher power of the inner self.

The understanding of the mythological teachings of the postures allows the practitioner to develop insight into the character and energy of each posture by understanding its presiding deity and enabling them to assume the role of that deity, thus allowing that cosmic force to be awakened within their consciousness. Therefore, along with the practice of the postures the practitioner should also study the mythology and teachings of the particular deity in order to gain insight into the feeling of the god or goddess of the posture. The gods and goddesses (Neteru) are in reality symbols of cosmic forces in nature and in the mind, which if understood and cultivated, cause a human being to develop their latent divine (Neteru) qualities, thus, engendering higher consciousness and spiritual enlightenment.

The practice of the postures should be seen as a journey of self-discovery and not as a chore or obligation simply to keep the physical body fit. That attitude will yield only limited results. The workout may be understood as a series of phases leading from Death to life, from before Creation to after Creation and from the Lower Self to the Higher.

The Beginning: Before Creation

In the beginning there were no forms, no Creation. There was only non-existence, but non-existence means absence of created objects (planets, stars, matter, the elements, etc.) and not absence of existence itself. The spirit was, is, and always will be and that spirit is symbolized by the Mummy (Karast) which is physically dead. The gods Asar and Anpu-Apuat preside over the dead mummy and from death life springs forth. This is the divine resurrection.

1- Karast (Mummy) Pose

Phase 1: Creation

As you perform the postures you will learn about and discover Creation. This is accomplished through the following poses.

2- Nefertem Lotus Pose

Nefertem is God in the form of the child, the innocence of creation as symbolized by the new born sun. He springs forth from the **Primeval Ocean** and sits atop the Lotus which is Creation itself, as its master. As God brought Creation into being through sound, or the word, which creates vibration or movement, so to the Journey of Enlightenment through the Thef Neteru (postures of the gods and goddesses) is begun with **Words Of Power** which set the proper vibrational tone to the environment, propitiate the presence of the cosmic forces to be discovered, harnessed and cultivated. If you have difficulty sitting in the lotus pose you may use the half lotus or the cross-legged posture.

WORDS OF POWER

You may use any words of power you were initiated into by your teacher or you may use those listed below.* You may add additional words of power in accordance with your inner feeling. Chant for five to ten minutes.

Om

(The universal Hekau or mantram of the Higher Self)

Anetej Neteru, Akhu Neteru, Dua Neteru

(Homage to the gods and goddesses, Glorious spirits they are, Adorations to them.

*See the book Initiation Into Egyptian Yoga for more Words of Power. You may also take this opportunity to practice breathing exercises here.

3- Nun Pose.

Nun is the Primeval Ocean from which all creation arises. The aspirant should understand that Creation already existed as unformed matter before it came into being. Unformed matter was given form by ideas, will and sound of God. Nothing is Created, only transformed from already previously existing essence. God Creates using his very own essence just as a human being creates the dream world during a dream from their very own mental essence. This "essence of God" is also referred to as the Neteru (gods and goddesses or *cosmic forces*) emanating from Pa Neter (The Supreme Being).

Words of Power during the practice of individual postures.

You may also use words of power as you practice the individual postures. The Mysticism of the Neteru involves the task of discovering them within yourself. This is the most powerful and highest form of Yoga practice, seeing yourself as one with the divine. This means learning about the neteru, acting like them, talking like them, feeling like them and finally being them. This is the most important aspect of all Kemetic (Ancient Egyptian) ritual systems and it is so because of its power to transforms a human being. As you believe so you become. If you believe you are a lowly human being you will think, feel and act that way and your life will be a reflection of that limitation and degradation. If you understand you are more than that you will discover more, your true identity. This process is called yoga and the end or goal of this process is called spiritual enlightenment, resurrection. Therefore, as you practice the postures you should see yourself as embodying the principles of the presiding deity of that posture. This is why it is important to understand the myths related to each of the neteru.

Egyptian Yoga Exercise is more than physical exercise. It is a ritual system of **Forms and Special Movements for becoming Divine**, one with the gods and goddesses and ultimately discovering that these gods and goddesses or cosmic forces, are in reality emanations from your innermost self. Thus you may utter the words **"Nuk pu"** and the name of the presiding deity as you go into each posture. For example, as you enter the Aset pose say "Nuk pu Aset, Nuk pu Aset" and so forth.

4- Shu Pose

Shu represents space and air, which separates heaven and earth but which also sustains life. Therefore breathing in this and all exercises is very important.

Then you will discover how Creation is sustained.

5- Warm Up –Preparing to Sustain Creation. Warm up is very important before going into any posture so as not to hurt any muscles or tendons, etc.

You will discover how Creation is separated into heaven and earth. (**Nut and Geb**)

6- Journey of Ra Pose Series

The Journey of Ra Pose Series is actually a journey within the larger journey of the whole program. It means understanding the cycle of daily creation through which God sustains Creation at every moment. Creation is not just an event that occurred billions of years ago. It is an ongoing process. Every day you journey in the physical world through your mind and physical body and through the astral world when you dream at night. Your desire and will

and your movement are what sustain your reality just as the constant movement of the spirit sustains Creation all the time. Coming into harmony with this means discovering the power to create a better life for yourself by taking control of your power in every moment of your life.

Phase 2: The Earth

Then you will discover the earth (gross-lower-physical nature) aspect of your own personality through the following postures.

7-8 Shoulder-stand Pose - Plough Pose,
9- Wheel Pose,
10- Fish Pose
11- Forward Bend Pose
12- Spinal Twist Pose

 These poses primarily focus on the physical spine since it is the structure which allows the body to function. Flexibility of the spine means physical health and mental health. Constriction and calcification or weakness of the spine means pain and disease (physical and mental). These postures affect the mind because they promote the health and flexibility of the spinal nerves which in turn affect the mind, and the psycho-spiritual energy centers, which exist in the Astral Body.

Phase 3: Transition Poses

The transition poses assist a spiritual aspirant in moving from the Earth Series postures towards the Higher Self. Now that Creation has been engendered and sustained and the Earth aspect of life (gross) has been explored and glorified it is time to begin the journey of discovering the subtle aspect of life. The transition poses are:

13- Selket –Scorpion Pose
14- Sebek –Crocodile Pose
15– Arat- Cobra Pose
16- Horemacket –Sphinx Pose
17- Heru – Horus Pose and variations

Heru is the supreme defender of truth, righteousness and justice. He is the successful spiritual aspirant. Therefore, he represents virtue, honor and invincible will. He is the perfect balance between the higher and lower self and he therefore leads the spiritual aspirant into the inner shrine of the spirit, the Higher Self.

18– Henu Pose Series

The Henu Pose Series is optional in the general practice of the Thef Neteru System of psycho-spiritual exercises. However, it should be part of the advanced program of practice. The Henu Form is a series of postures performed to pay homage to the Divine. Its movements are slow and deliberate as well as graceful, creating a devotional feeling between practitioner and the Higher Self. Anpu, Heru, Set and others divinities preside over this posture and it is great honor to perform it.

Phase 4: The Higher Self Poses

The Higher Self is the subtle, expansive aspect of existence. It is presided over by the goddess in three special forms. Nut– expansive, infinite self. Maat– virtuous self. Aset– intuitional wisdom of self. Thus we have the following poses:

19- Nut Pose
20- Maat Pose and
21- Aset Winged Pose
22– Aset Sitting Pose
23-Aset Embrace Pose

Phase 5: Establishment Poses

The establishment poses are designed to help the practitioner become established in the benefits derived from the teachings and exercises of the previous phases. The Establishment Poses are:

24– Djed Pose
25- Headstand Pose
26- Khepri— Scarab Pose
27– Shti (Mummy) Pose

Sheti means the body which is prepared for resurrection. This pose is used for the final relaxation and meditation of the session.

Closing Words of Power

Om Hetep Hetep Hetep
(Om Peace, Peace, Peace.)

Tjef Neteru as A Dynamic System of Varied Modes of Spiritual Practice

The *Tjef neteru Sema Paut Neteru* system is actually an extremely flexible and dynamic method of spiritual practice as it can be performed in one of several modes to suit the needs of the particular attendants, the particular teaching style of the leader or the purpose of the session. (introductory session, physical workout session, mythological emphasis session, meditative emphasis session, etc.)

The program may be practiced as follows:

I.   **A Physical Workout Session**
   a. The postures may be practiced with a lower or higher number of repetitions in order to engender a more basic (beginners) or intense (intermediate or advanced) physical workout.

II.   **A Mythological/Ritual Workout**
   a. The program may be practiced in such a way that the mythic teachings are imparted throughout so that the practitioners gain an understanding of the psychospiritual principals to be cultivated. (combines the benefits of the Kemetic Spiritual Wisdom with the physical workout benefits)

III.   **A Meditative Session**
   a. The program may be practiced as a meditative session by reducing the number of repetitions and holding the postures for a longer period of time while being led through guided imagery into a silent reflection on each posture.

IV.   **A Meditative Form**
   a. This form of practice is for proficient practitioners. There is no guided imagery or instruction given by the leader except the name of the posture. The practitioners skillfully move from one posture to another in a flowing and balanced manner, thereby developing the inner spontaneous movement of the Neteru cosmic consciousness, an intuitional harmonizing of the individual with the cosmic.

"Smai Tawi"
(Egyptian Yoga)

Pose 1~The Beginning: Before Creation

Left: The Ancient Egyptian Supreme Being in the form of the evening sun (Tem), encircled by the serpent of "Many Faces" (infinity and multiplicity). The Serpent symbolizes the power or Life Force through which Creation is engendered. The Serpent, "Mehen" lives in the primeval ocean out of which Creation arises. Note the symbol, ᔕ. It is an Ancient Egyptian determinative used to signify "limb," "flesh," "parts of the body." There are three symbols at the feet of Ra and next to these are the heads of the serpent. In mystical terms the meaning is that from the singular essence arise the three aspects, the Trinity, and from these arise the multiplicity of Creation. Thus, Creation is the very flesh or body of God. From his head is emerging Khepri, the Creator of the universe, who performs the actual act of creation. It is important to understand that the creation act is not something that happened once long ago. Khepri is said to create the new day every day. Thus, the implication is that creation is a continuous process which sustains the universe at every moment just as you sustain your dream world at every moment during a dream..

Visualize that you are that spirit, completely still, with all the potential to manifest and create anything you want.

See yourself resting on the great serpent which lives in the Primeval Ocean. See your body as a dead mummy but with a burgeoning Life Force power deep down.

Visualize the journey ahead, the creation that is to follow, and marvel at that wondrous power of the Divine within you to enliven the body and sustain Creation.

Stay completely still in this posture for 2 minutes, relaxing every muscle. Do not move even if you want to scratch. Stay absolutely still as if your body were dead.

Sit up now and come to the Lotus Posture, to begin the process of coming to life and Creating your world, your peace, your health and your spiritual enlightenment.

The Sitting Poses

(Fig. 1)

(Fig. 2)

(Fig. 3)

The Lotus Pose

Ancient Egyptian Practicing the Lotus Pose

The Easy Pose

(Fig. 4)

(Fig. 4A)

(Fig. 6)

(Fig. 5)

Fig. 7

The Sitting Poses

Now sit in the easy pose or the lotus pose to practice a few breathing exercises. You can use The easy pose (Fig. 4) is best for beginners, unless you are very flexible, because it does not put undue strain on the muscles. An alternative posture is to sit with your legs folded under you as shown in Fig. 4A. As you progress, you may eventually begin to practice the lotus pose (Fig. 1) for your exercises and meditations. The lotus pose requires much practice and concentration. Once it is mastered, it is a good posture for meditation because it is centered, stable and it keeps the back straight which maintains the alignment of the energy centers of the vertebrae column.

The Lotus flower (Figs. 2,3,5,6) has deep mystical symbolism in both Ancient Egypt and India. It relates to the spiritual aspirant who develops detachment and dispassion from the world since it sits in the muddy water but is not touched or affected by the mud. It is ever pure and detached. This is how life is to be lived. Detachment from the illusory pleasures of the world allows the mind to be calm and concentrated for spiritual study and meditation. These in turn lead the spiritual aspirant to discover the infinite realms of the inner Self.

Figure 7 is The King sitting on the throne. This posture as well as Fig. 1, 4, and 4A, may be used for meditation.

The sitting poses are the beginning of your spiritual exercises. Therefore, you should begin by invoking some auspicious prayers, chants or your favorite utterances to propitiate positive energies during this time. A simple and universal practice is to chant "Om," "Om," "Om,""Om,"etc.

OTHER POSTURES

Left: Knees bent while resting the folded elbows on the knees.

Right: sitting on heels with toes extended and hands on the thighs.

Proper Breathing and Deep Yogic Breathing

Fig. A

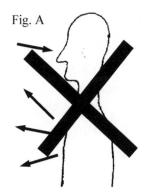

Above: Chest breathing.
Below: Abdominal
breathing.

Fig. B

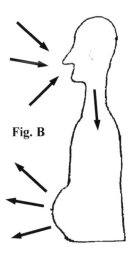

Fig. C

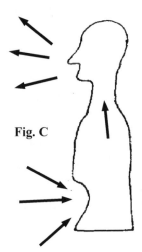

Proper Breathing

Proper breathing is one effective way to store and accumulate vital Life Force energy in the body. Other means are control of emotions, thoughts, actions, etc. Proper breathing is a practice that should be used especially before and during meditation since it acts to harmonize the energies of the mind and consequently also the mind.

Most people in the modern world do not know how to breathe properly. Most people (especially males) have learned to breathe by pushing out the chest in a "manly" or "macho" fashion. This mode of breathing is harmful for many reasons. The amount of air taken in is less and vital cosmic energy is reduced and becomes stagnant in the subtle vital energy channels, resulting in physical and mental diseases. The stagnation of the flow of energy through the body has the effect of grounding one's consciousness to the physical realities rather than allowing the mind and body to operate with lightness and subtlety.

"Belly breathing" or abdominal breathing massages the internal organs and develops Life Force energy (Sekhem, Chi or Prana). It will be noticed that it is your natural breathing pattern when you lie down on your back. Instruction is as follows: A- Breathe in and push the stomach out. B- Breathe out and pull the stomach in. This form of breathing is to be practiced at all times, not just during meditation. It allows the natural Life Force in the air to be rhythmically supplied to the body and nervous system. This process is indispensable in the achievement of physical health and mental-spiritual power to control the mind (meditation).

<u>Deep (Yogic) Breathing—The 3 Part Breath:</u> Breathe as in the Proper Breathing technique, except more deeply. Inhale and push the abdomen out, then without releasing the breath, again inhale a little deeper filling the lungs in the chest area, and again, without releasing the breath, inhale deeper still, filling the area of the lungs under the shoulders. With this last inhalation, the shoulders should rise up a little, naturally. Control your exhalation so that it is soft and smooth, and twice the time it took for the inhalation. Exhale first by releasing the shoulders and letting the air out from the top of the lungs, then release the chest and let the air out from the middle lung area, and finally pull the abdomen in expelling all remaining air from the lungs. Repeat. The deep breathing technique allows you to take approximately 5 times the oxygen and Life Force Energy than the normal breath, thus revitalizing and cleansing the body and mind, and balancing the emotions (through the Serpent Power System).

Breathing exercise: With eyes closed, allow the abdomen to expand as you breathe in. Visualize that you are taking in Life Force energy along with the air. See it remaining in your body as you expel the air. Visualize that all the nutrients of the air are being used and that impurities are being carried away.

Alternate Nostril Breathing

Prior to your practice of yoga postures and meditation, you should practice *ALTERNATE NOS-TRIL BREATHING.* There are opposing forces (poles) of energy in the human body. These forces are related to mental energy, the emotions, and mental and physical health. When these poles are out of balance, various mental, emotional and physical problems can arise. When harmonized, they allow you to experiencing vitality, health, mental calm, concentration and inner peace. The study of these forces is related to the Uraeus Serpent of Egypt and the Kundalini Serpent Yoga systems of India. For now, simply follow the instructions below and you will begin to feel improved health and vitality. As you study the deeper implications of the breath, more teachings will be given to enhance your practice.

The opposing energy poles of the body, Uatchet (Udjat, Utchat) and Nekhebet, can be balanced by practicing a simple *ALTERNATE NOSTRIL BREATHING* exercise. These Ancient Egyptian names are symbolic of the opposing energies that flow through the subtle spirit body and energy centers of every human being. They are also referred to as the solar channel and the lunar channel, or the Pingala and the Ida Nadis (energy channels) in the Indian Kundalini system, respectively. The solar breath (Uatchet, through the right nostril) is heating to the body and is therefore useful when physical activity is to be performed. Also, the solar breath is useful when there is disease in the body. At this time, breathing through the solar channel will heat up the body and assist it in overcoming the disease process. Therefore, if there is illness, the left nostril should be blocked off for given periods of time. This may also be practiced before going to bed. When going to bed one should lay on the left side when falling asleep in order to cause the breath to flow through the right nostril. The lunar breath (Nekhebet, through the left nostril) is cooling to the body. However, unless one is well advanced in the practice of yoga, one should practice the *ALTERNATE NOSTRIL BREATHING* which harmonizes both the solar and lunar channels, therefore balancing the energy of the mind and body.

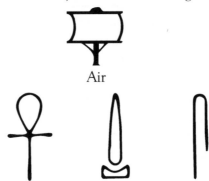

Air

Ankh, Oodja, Seneb = Life, Vitality, Health -The Special Kemetic Benediction

The air contains vital Life Force energy which is subtler than the air itself. The term, ⵎ, oodja the central sign in the Ancient Egyptian benediction, *Life, Vitality and Health,* gives us a very important teaching in reference to the process of human existence on earth. The sign signifies "fire drill" or an instrument used to start a fire or the commencement of the burning process. Used in this manner the idea that is given is that the Divine Life Process, ☥ (Ankh), engenders a fire (*oodja,* vitality) which courses through the body and promotes health, ⵊ, (*seneb*).

Vitality is what gives the impetus to life. It is the force, which sustains and gives a person the

Alternate Nostril Breathing

will to live. If there is no vitality the entire personality is depressed and there is no enjoyment of life. Vitality sustains the immune system and the immune system keeps external as well as internal agents (bacteria, viruses, poisons, waste material, etc.) from disturbing the course of life. Vitality may also be referred to by the term Life Force or the Kemetic term Sekhem. Therefore, the following formula may be applied to the understanding of the inner processes that sustain life:

Vitality = immunity = health = life.

Oodja, (subtle essence of vitality), and Seneb (health), allow one to have Sekhem or Physical Power.

Skhem divine power
-power of nature

ALTERNATE NOSTRIL BREATHING:

Sitting in a comfortable posture, using the right hand, bend the index and middle finger toward the palm while leaving the thumb, fourth and fifth (pinkie) fingers extended (position 1). Using the thumb to close off the right nostril, breath in (inhalation) through the left nostril while holding the right one closed (position 2), then close both nostrils using the fourth finger to close the left nostril leaving the pinkie finger extended and the other two fingers remaining bent (position 3). Release the thumb from the right nostril and exhale through the right nostril (position 4). Next, breath in through the right nostril while holding the left one closed (position 4). Close both nostrils by holding the right nostril close with the thumb (position 3) and retain the breath for a short time, then release the fourth finger from the left nostril and breathe out through the left nostril (position 2). This constitutes one cycle of the *Alternate Nostril Breathing* exercise. The ratio of inhalation: retention: exhalation should be 2:8:4 to begin, working up to 4:16:8. You may repeat a hekau (mantra) such as "OM" while performing this exercise. Continue in this way for five minutes at the beginning, gradually building up to fifteen minutes or longer as needed. The *Alternate Nostril Breathing* exercise is an excellent way to balance the body's energies. The energies may also be balanced other ways, such as by controlling the emotions, remaining calm and engaging one's self in activities that are in harmony with one's consciousness (hobbies, job, recreation).

| Position 1 | Position 2 | Position 3 | Position 4 |

Pose 2~ Nefertem:
The Divine Child of Creation

Forms of Heru as Ne-
fertem (Neferatum)

Above: Nefertem is Heru in the form of the sun god as Creator. He presides over the Lotus of Creation which is the universe itself. The lotus emanates from the Primeval Ocean of formless, undifferentiated matter.

Nefertem means: "Beautiful Completion" or the culmination of all things which owe their existence to the Self or spirit. All things are completed in God. As a child Nefertem symbolizes the
morning sun which engenders the coming into being of life to the world at dawn. The finger pointing to the mouth symbolizes divine consciousness which expresses as sound. Sound or the word,
through its vibrations and intent, brings forth the forming
of undifferentiated matter (primeval ocean) into form (Creation-the lotus). The Lotus, upon which
the Divine Child sits, emanates from the Primeval Ocean. Therefore, all matter which composes
the world comes from that ocean-everything comes from and is made up of the same essence. The
sitting atop the lotus also symbolizes the mastery of the spirit over, as well as detachment and transcendence from Creation.

Be seated in the lotus posture, or any comfortable cross legged posture – with back straight.

Next raise your right arm and place the tip of your index finger on the center of your lips. See yourself as the spirit which brings creation into being just as your mind creates ideas from unformed subtle matter. God brings forth physical creation from unformed elements (gross matter).

Next place your hand back on your knee and begin uttering the Words of Power which bring Creation into being, the names of God. You may use the chants below or any others you may find in the book Initiation Into Egyptian Yoga. Or you may use any other words which you have been initiated into by your spiritual teacher or which have special spiritual significance to you.

Om, Om, Om, Om
Dua (adorations) Ra, Dua Ra, Dua Ra, Khepera
Om Asar Aset Heru

Next begin seeing the objects around you as forms which have been created from primeval matter itself.

Next close your eyes and see yourself as assuming the role of Nefertem. See yourself as being the supreme ruler who is sitting atop Creation, as its monarch but also detached from it as well.

Ancient Egyptian Practicing the Lotus Pose

Pose 3- Nun: The Creation

Above: The god Nun lifting the Divine Boat out of the Primeval Ocean and thereby engendering Creation.

Nun is the Primeval Ocean itself. It is at once a deity as well as part of Ra's very essence. The practice of the Nun Posture requires **(Position 1)** that the practitioner should bring the hands together in a squatting position. This symbolizes unity of the opposites and self-containment. Then visualize yourself as being submerged below the surface of the ocean.

Imagine that there is no world and that everything is like an ocean, homogenous and peaceful. There is no sky, no heaven and earth, no sun, only water all around you. Exhale.

Position 2: Now raise up as you breathe in as if you are pushing up and out of the surface of the water.

Position 3: Raise up further and continue breathing in and pushing up higher. And now visualize that your movement up and above the surface of the water is bringing the sky and the earth and air into being.

Position 4: Complete the inhalation and extend your arms fully, standing straight.

Reverse: Now come back down as you breath out. Gradually lower your arms until they come back together and you reach the squatting position once more. Exhale fully and begin raising up once more. Repeat 3-5 times.

Pose 4: The Shu Posture

The
God
Shu: Air
and
Space.

Pose 4: The Shu Posture

SHU - Space and Air

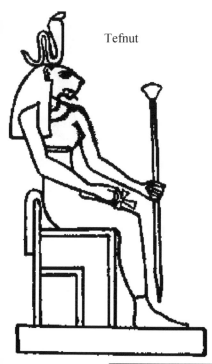

Tefnut

Shu is the divinity which was sent by Ra, the Supreme Being, to separate Geb and Nut (earth and heaven). So Shu is the instrument by which the Divine Self caused the world to come into its present form which sustains all life. Thus, Shu represents air, space or ether. Air contains a subtle Life Force energy which sustains life. This subtle energy is called Sekhem. It is presided over by Shu's consort, Tefnut. Tefnut represents moisture, such as when it rains. Rain allows plants to grow and it brings water for people to live.

Tefnut is the powerful strength which is in the ocean of creation and she is the source of vitality for all living things.

Inhale deeply, raising up on your toes as you raise your arms up along side your body, bring them over your head, and then, lowering your arms down along side your body and your feet back onto the ground (flat), exhale as you come down.

Breath freely and deeply. See yourself as the creator of your own life, the sustainer of your reality. Breath in the universe and see yourself communing with cosmic life itself.

Whisper as you breath out *Shu...Shu...Shu...Shu...*

Pose 5~ Warm Up

(Fig. 1)

(Fig. 2)

(Fig. 3)

WARM UP AND DANCING

Now first we will begin with some warm up exercises. It is very important to warm up the body before doing any kind of exercise so that we won't hurt any of our tendons, ligaments or muscles.

(Fig. 1) Standing with feet approximately 1 1/2 to 2 feet apart, begin swinging the body gently from side to side, four times to the right and four times to the left. Inhale as you turn to the right and exhale as you turn to the left. Try to twist you body as much as you can so you can look behind you. Just allow the body to flow with the movement and allow your mind to also flow with the movement as if you are dancing. Feel the air as it passes around your arms and hands. Very good.

(Fig. 2) Hands on the waist and bending from side to side, four times to the left and four times to the right. As you go through the video or book you will be seeing some Egyptian pictographs (pictures of steles showing these very exercises we are doing now).

(Fig. 3) Keeping the hands on the waist, bend backwards and forwards, four times in each direction. If you are using the video and would like to perform a particular exercise for a longer period of time, you can also stop the video at any point.

Keeping the pelvis still and facing forwards, rotate the top of the body in a circular fashion: Bend forward, bend to the right, bend backwards, bend to the left, forward, etc. Circle to the right three times, then to the left three times.

Pause for a moment to relax, hands together in the Hetep Posture, (as when saying a prayer), symbolizing the union of the Higher and lower self. Close your eyes and as you inhale, think about the symbolism of Hetep: Supreme Peace, Harmony and Unity with everything. Feel that you are surrounded by that peace. Feel that you are one with everything in creation. Inhale deeply, feeling that you are inhaling peace and exhale and release tension from the body and mind. Repeat three times, being sure to use the proper breathing technique.

Now hands to the side. We are going to warm up the neck. It is very important to warm up the neck before doing some of the exercises we are going to do today. Move it back and forth from side to side, backwards and forwards, four time in each direction. Now roll the head in a circle to the left four times. Repeat to the right. Pause for a moment.

Pose 6: The Journey of Ra

Our next exercise will be *The Journey of Ra Posture Series.* This posture holds deep mystical symbolism involving the Ancient Egyptian deities Ra, Nut, and Osiris and the evolution of the individual Ba (soul). It incorporates *The Nut Forward Bend* and *The Cobra Pose,* which will also be performed later on as separate postures.

In the Ancient Egyptian creation story, the goddess Nut consumes Ra, as symbolized by Tem, the setting sun in the evening, and Nut also gives birth to Ra, as symbolized by Khepri the rising sun in the morning. The time between when Nut consumes Ra and when she gives birth to him, that is, the time between dusk and dawn, Ra is said to travel in the Underworld (Duat). There are many deep implications to this teaching of the Underworld.

In one aspect, the Underworld represents the subtle world or astral plane where your dream or astral (out of body) experiences take place. It is also the plane where the soul of an unenlightened personality goes when the body dies, to have heavenly or hellish experiences, depending on its karmic fate. There is another aspect of the Underworld known as Amenta, which represents the abode of Osiris. This is where enlightened souls go when their bodies die. When you enter into deep dreamless sleep, you enter into this abode of Osiris, however because you are not enlightened, your experience in this realm is as if shrouded by a veil. This "veil" is referred to as the veil of Isis. It represents the ignorant (unenlightened) mind which cannot experience the Transcendental Reality which exists all around it, all the time, and is its very nature. So Isis represents Creation, which is nothing but a manifestation of the Divine Self, Ra (or Osiris). When the mind is enlightened, the veil of Isis lifts and one experiences only the Divine Self. There is no more duality, no more distinguishing Creation from God, and vice versa. This veiling power of the ignorant mind carries over into the dream state and the deep, dreamless sleep state. So when you wake up you only know that you feel rejuvenated, that you had a good night's rest, but you have no knowledge of what took place.

However, through the process of deep yogic meditation you are able to go to Amenta, the abode of Osiris, and experience the supreme all-encompassing Self, your own true nature, as profound peace, bliss and expansion in consciousness, with conscious awareness. When you attain enlightenment, you will forever-more abide, consciously, in the peace and bliss of the Supreme Self, Osiris, whether you are involved in the waking, dream or deep sleep states of consciousness.

Pose 6: The Journey of Ra

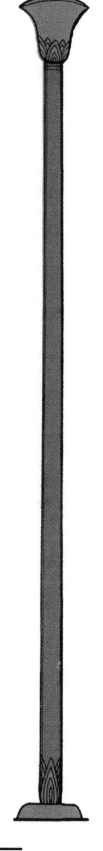

The Journey of Ra also symbolizes the cycle of reincarnation and the process of transmigration of the individual (unenlightened) soul. The birth of Ra in the morning in the eastern sky symbolizes the birth of an individual into the world of time and space as an ego-personality, that is, a personality identified with the body, mind and ego as being the totality of his/her being. Ra's journey from the eastern horizon to the western symbolizes the life of an individual, and Ra's setting in the western sky followed by his being consumed by Nut symbolizes the death experience of the individual. The after-death experience is symbolized by Ra journeying into the Underworld. In yogic mysticism, the consciousness of the individual does not die when the body of that individual dies, because the essence of that individual is immortal and eternal. In the Underworld (Duat, astral plane), the soul (unenlightened consciousness) of the individual encounters heavenly or hellish experiences depending on if the individual lived a life of virtue (spiritual principles) or vice (egoism), respectively. After journeying in the astral plane, Ra again emerges from Nut as she gives birth to him in the form of the morning sun. So too, the consciousness of the individual which survives the death of the body becomes born into a new body based on the karmic needs of the soul and once again enters the world of time and space, to repeat this cycle of life, death, astral experiences, birth, etc., over and over again, until enlightenment is attained. When enlightenment is attained, the soul of the individual which is now one with the Universal Soul joins with Osiris in Amenta after the death of the body, never to be reborn into the world of time and space again. It abides in eternity and immortality.

With respect to one's spiritual discipline or *Sheti*, Ra, as symbolized by the sun, represents the yogic qualities of *consistency*, *sustained effort* and *perseverance*. We always know exactly when the sun is going to rise and when it is going to set; it is always consistent. It never decides that it is too tired to rise when it is supposed each morning to perform its duties. And it never overindulges, staying out longer in the evening because it is having such a good time that it does not want to retire. It sets when it is time for it to retire for the evening, and it rises when it is time for it to do so. This quality of consistency is one of the key qualities an aspirant must develop to be successful in their practice of their program of spiritual discipline or Sheti. An aspirant must strive to be consistent in the time and place of the practice of spiritual disciplines, to the extent that it is possible to do so. Meditation should be practiced in the early hours of the morning between 4 to 6 A.M., before sunrise.

11

12

12a

10

9

8

7

The Journey
of
Ra

The Journey of Ra

The sun also never becomes tired and bored of doing the same thing over and over again, rising and setting, rising and setting, rising and setting, etc., and therefore, quits performing its duty, offering excuses as to why it was not possible for it to accomplish its task.   Just like each day you eat, you drink, you brush your teeth, you shower, and perform certain other daily tasks, over and over again, you need to exert self effort day by day to perform your Sheti. You should not justify not performing your spiritual discipline by saying "Well, I did it yesterday and I'll do it again tomorrow, but today I want to take a break." Did you take a break from talking today because you talked yesterday? Did you take a break from eating or drinking today because you ate and drank yesterday? Did you not wash your face today because you washed it yesterday? So the mind has numerous tricks it plays on the unwary aspirant. You should strive to be like Ra, to perform your duties unceasingly and effortlessly, and your personal program of Sheti is your most important duty of your life, so you need to make time for it daily, and put forth every effort to be consistent in your practice.

In the Ancient Egyptian creation story, it is said that each day as Ra emerges in the eastern sky, he has to do battle with the negative forces of Set and his fiendish friends who are constantly trying to stop the Barque of Ra from moving on in its journey across the heavens. If the Barque of Ra stops moving, creation comes to an end. Knowing that he will encounter evil forces, Ra perseveres each day, performing his duty. In this aspect he exemplifies *perseverance in the face of adversity.* Perseverance in the face of adversity is a very important quality which an aspirant must strive to attain. Studying and practicing yoga does not mean that your external life will necessarily become easier and you won't have to face certain challenges in the form of adverse situations. It does mean that through practicing the spiritual disciplines of yoga, you will gain insight into your true nature, and thus the world around you. This insight will allow you to, in effect, keep your head above water in calm seas as well as the rough seas of life. In other words, like Ra, you will be able to overcome Set and his evil friends in the form of your own egoism (Set) and its accompanying negative sentiments of anger, greed, insecurity, jealousy, fear and tension (Set's friends) which, each day, from the time you emerge from sleep in the morning, try to over power your spiritual awareness. Thus, like Ra, you must be constantly vigilant to not allow Set and his evil friends to interrupt your spiritual progress on the path to attaining Enlightenment.

Another yogic quality Ra, as symbolized by the sun, demonstrates is selfless service. We have discussed the importance of selfless service at length in our books, videos and tape series based on the teachings of Maat. We have empha-

The Journey of Ra

sized that an aspirant must incorporate performing selfless service for the benefit of humanity as part of their spiritual discipline. In the traditional yogic system, this includes devoting some time to help your spiritual preceptor in the dissemination of wisdom as to the nature of the Self to those who desire it. This form of selfless service is very pure because it leads those who practice the teachings of yoga to uproot the very tree of pain and suffering which human beings experience. This does not mean that other forms of selfless service should not be practiced as well. If someone is hungry or thirsty, knowledge of the Self is most likely not going to help them whereas food and water would. Therefore, balance and common sense must always be observed, and practicing one form of selfless service should not negate other forms of selfless service which you may be called upon to perform.

Ra, in the form of the sun, exemplifies true selfless service. He knows how important it is in sustaining life on earth, yet he puts forth his life-giving essence without asking for anything in return. He does not hoard his energy, demanding that unless he is paid his due by humankind, he will cease to work. He does not accept bribes, shining more on those who have more money. He shines on all equally, and he does this everyday. He does not force his will on humankind. If people choose to stay in their houses or remain in bed all day with their blinds close, he does not become upset and force his way in. He is there, splendorous, but detached and dispassionate, and those who wish to partake of what he has to offer are welcome to do so. Those who wish to thank him may do so, but he does not depend on or require the gratitude of humankind to perform his duty. He shines on everyone freely, without judgment. He does not say "I'm going to shine on you but not you, because you did this negative deed."

Ra gives himself freely to all. Without this life-giving essence the earth would not be here; it could not exist. So in the morning when you wake up and go outside and see and feel the sun as it shines on you, feel the warmth and allow the life-giving energy to penetrate into your very being so that throughout the day when you are called upon to help others, you can do the same, give freely of yourself, willingly, without asking for anything in return.

So, keep these qualities of bliss, peace, consistency, self-effort, repeated effort, sustained effort, perseverance and selfless service in mind as you prepare to perform *The Journey of Ra Posture Flow*. Feel that you embody all of these divine qualities. As you flow through these postures, feel the energy flowing smoothly and unhampered throughout your entire body. Try to perform all your duties each day with this same free flowing manner, not allowing the ego to step in.

The Journey of Ra

Strive to the ultimate abode of selfless service. Strive to be like Ra. Feel that you are the abode of selflessness as you perform your actions. Dedicate all your actions to Ra as a symbolic gesture of selfless service. Feel that all actions being performed by you are really being performed by your Higher Self, Ra. Allow all actions to lead your mind to think of Ra, the ultimate abode of selfless service.

THE JOURNEY OF RA

Now, stand up on the front of your mat to begin this exercise series. It is a little intricate so just take your time. It consists of twelve positions, however, the last six positions are basically the reverse postures of the first six.

(1) Exhale and bring your hands together in *The Hetep Pose*, the prayer position. (2) Inhale, raising your arms in front of you and then over your head, bend backwards . Reach back as far as you can, keeping your pelvis tucked in and arching your upper back, and symbolically take hold of Ra (sun disk) to remove him from the sky (setting sun). (3) Bring Ra down to begin his journey in the Underworld as you bend forwards, trying to keep your back straight and your arms extended straight, in alignment with your neck. Bending all the way down, folding over, bring your hands to your feet, placing them (flat...if flexible enough) on the floor alongside your feet. If you need to you may bend your knees. (4) Inhale your right foot back pointing the toes behind you, and raise your head up, looking back as far as you can, pushing your pelvis down to give a good stretch. Balance yourself with your palms placed flat on the floor or on the tips of your fingers if you are not very flexible (but eventually working to place the palms flat on the floor). (5) Tuck the toes of the right leg under, and holding the breath, place your left leg back, alongside the right leg and come up into *The Nut Pose*, an inverted V. Try to push the heels of your feet flat on the floor and your head down between your arms to give a good stretch. This is where goddess Nut consumes Ra. (6) Keeping your buttocks in the air, exhale and lower your knees to the floor, pointing your toes, then arching the back lower the chest and chin (beginners) or forehead (more advanced) to the ground, as you journey into the Underworld. (7) Now inhale and push up with your arms, keeping the elbows bent, raising your head and chest up and arch backwards as far as you can, keeping your abdomen and pelvis on the floor, as you raise yourself up in consciousness as you glide into *The Cobra Pose*. Keep your elbows tucked into your sides as much as possible and focus your practice of The *Cobra Pose* at the sixth energy center, the seat of higher consciousness, at the point between the eyes (the Mer energy center or Ajna chakra).

The Journey of Ra

The second half of the posture series is performed by reversing the steps in the first half. Now you are going back up into *The Nut Pose*. (8) Exhale, and as you come up into *The Nut Pose*, an inverted V, pressing your heels and head to the floor. This symbolizes Nut giving birth to Ra as he emerges from the Underworld, and now you are going to set him in the sky. (9) Inhale and bring the right foot all the way forward between the hands, looking up and back. If you cannot bring the right foot all the way forward, grab the ankle with the right hand and move it into position. Again, push down on the pelvis while looking up and back to give a good stretch. (10) Exhale and place the left foot forward between the hands and straighten the legs so that you are folded over, hands flat on the floor, fingers in line with the toes. (11) Inhale, and again keeping your arms extended and aligned with your neck and the back straight, raise up, bending forwards, then stretching straight up, and then all the way backwards, not allowing the pelvis to push forward but keeping it tucked in, reach over the head and place Ra back in the sky as the rising sun. (12) Exhale and lower your arms *The Hetep Pose*, then alongside your body. This is one cycle. Repeat using the left leg. You may alternate legs as you continue to perform more cycles. You may perform six to eight cycles according to your capacity, then relax in *The Mummy Pose* (13)
.

The Journey of Ra Posture is a good pose to wake yourself up in the morning and to jump start your metabolism, even if your don't have time to do the other postures. Try it instead of a cup of coffee. It relaxes and stretches all the muscles and joints in the body and massages the internal organs, so it is also a very good warm up exercise, and of course there is great spiritual benefit to be derived if you reflect on the mystical implications of the posture series.

Right: Ra traverses in his Barque over the body of Nut..

Pose 7~8: The Geb Plough Posture

The Ancient Egyptian god Geb performing the Plough Pose-from the ceiling in the ante-chamber to the resurrection room-Temple of Hetheru in Egypt, Africa.

1. Teṭ with the head of Osiris.

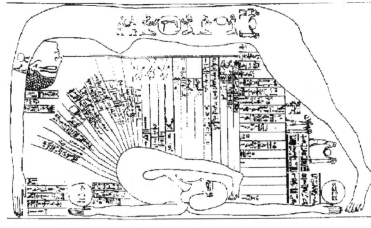

The Ancient Egyptian god Geb perform-

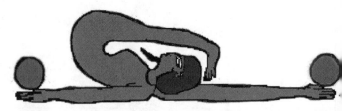

The Pillar of Asar is the spiritual spine of every human being. The plough posture strengthens, elongates the spine and awakens the spiritual Life Force.

Pose 7-8: The Geb Shoulderstand-Plough Posture

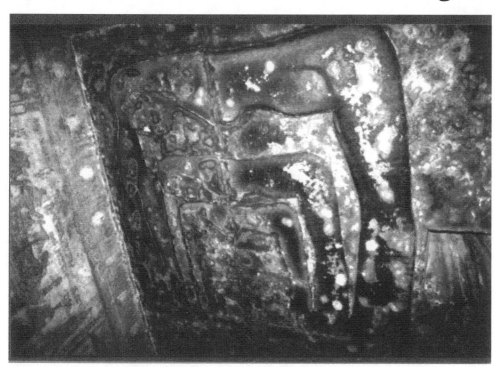

The Ancient Egyptian god Geb and Nut performing the Plough Pose and Forward Bend Pose-from the ceiling in the antechamber to the resurrection room-Temple of Hetheru in Egypt, Africa.

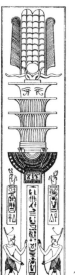

The Pillar of Asar .

Pose 7~8: The Geb Plough Posture

2

1

The Shoulder
Stand

Pose 7-8: The Geb Plough Posture

Next, we are going to practice the plough exercise. In the Egyptian Yoga Exercise program this is known as the Geb exercise. This is one of the exercises which Geb does, once he separated from Nut. This is an Earth exercise, meaning that it is for the entire physical body, but, specifically for the back as well as for the neck region and the neck spiritual center. In ancient Egyptian Yoga, the four upper spiritual energy centers are referred to as the "Back of Osiris," "Pillar of Osiris" or "The Vertebrae of the Initiate". There are several ancient Egyptian hieroglyphs related to *Arat*, The Uraeus or the Serpent Power or Life Force energy (Known as Kundalini in India) and the spiritual energy centers of the subtle astral body. They relate to the spinal column or vertebrae. Some of these are below:

Any exercise which is performed to benefit the spine will also be beneficial for the upper energy centers of the subtle spiritual body. However, when the exercises are performed with the special mythological and psychological insights given through a program of yoga instruction, the benefits are much greater.

Left: The hieroglyph of the "Vertebrae".

Bottom right: From the *"Egyptian Book of Coming Forth By Day,"* this episode is known as "The Slaughter." The soul of Ankhwahibre does battle with Apopis who is sitting atop the vertebrae (Back - Djed Pillar of Osiris) implying that Apopis seeks control of the spiritual energy present in the spiritual subtle channels of the back.

INSTRUCTIONS FOR THE PLOUGH POSE

Lay flat on your back. Now lifting both legs, keeping the knees straight, bring your knees over your stomach, to your chest, gradually help yourself up with your arms supporting yourself on your back and work yourself up to make your body straight. Before bending the legs over completely to the ground push straight up as you support your lower back. This is the shoulder stand. Now move your toes down to the floor, touching the ground with your toes behind your head. Do this posture according to your level of flexibility and do not force it.

Try to keep your knees straight. Now moving back up, gently bring the legs down and roll yourself out of this position and feel every section of your back as you do this. Now rest for a few minutes on your back. Take some deep breaths. Once again, remember to breathe with your belly.

Pose 9: The Wheel Pose

From ancient Egypt,
An Egyptian woman performing
the wheel pose in ancient times.

At left:
From
ancient
Egypt
The wheel
pose.

Pose 9: The Wheel Pose

The next posture is known as the cartwheel or wheel pose. It is beneficial for the arms, legs and the back.

Also, it is extremely beneficial to the psycho-spiritual energy centers which lie in the subtle spinal column. This posture stimulates the energy centers to promote spiritual awakening. This teaching is known as the Arat or Serpent Power. It is relates to the Cobra pose as well.

See the book "The Serpent Power" by Dr. Muata Ashby.

INSTRUCTION:

Lie on your back, arms behind the head, palms on the ground with fingers pointing toward your feet, feet up close to buttocks, now push up. Hold for as long as you can, then come down gently watching the breath. Breath in as you go up and breath out as you come down.

Now relax flat on your back with legs two feet apart and arms one foot apart from the body, breathing deeply as you relax. You are breathing the forces of Geb and Nut within our bodies together once again, as they were in the beginning, in harmony. The male and female principles, the opposites, heaven and earth are coming together within our bodies as Geb and Nut come together within our beings.

Pose 10: The Fish

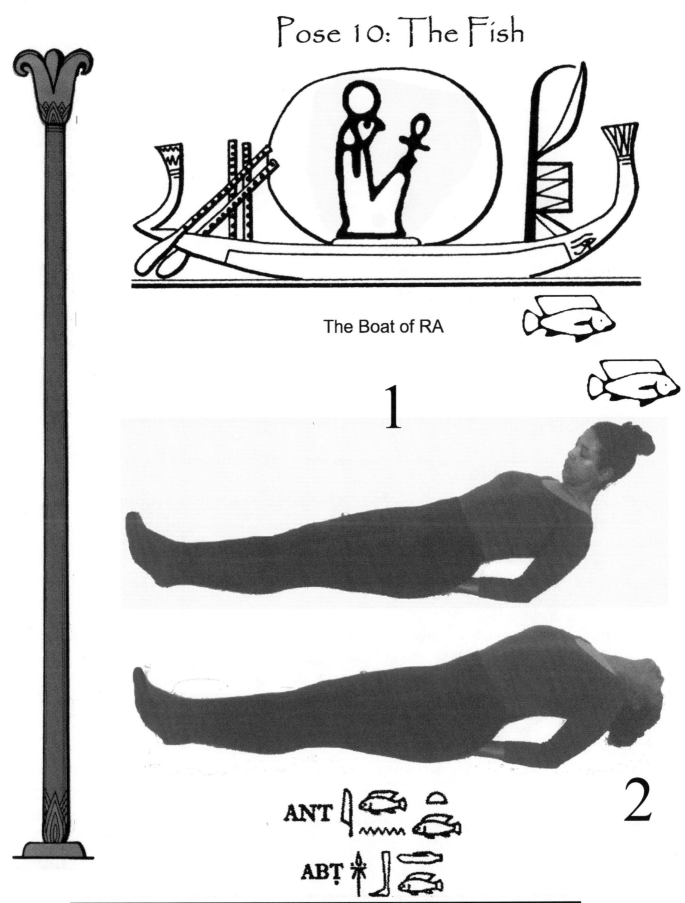

The Boat of RA

1

2

ANT

ABT

Pose 10: The Fish

In the creation story, there are two fish that guide the boat of Ra on its journey. As you perform this posture, feel that you are being led by the Spirit, the Higher Self, on this journey to the experience of oneness of enlightenment.

THE FISH POSE:

The Fish Pose is the counter pose for *The Shoulderstand Pose* and should ALWAYS be done after *The Shoulderstand Pose*. Begin from *The Mummy Pose*. Bring your legs together and place your arms alongside your body, palms up, your fingers barely under the outside of your thighs. Grab a hold of your thighs for leverage and gently raise your upper body as you come onto your elbows. Now arch your neck and upper spine backwards, bending your head back to bring the top of your head unto the floor behind you. Support your weight on your buttocks, elbows and the top of your head. In this position, your chest cavity is very expanded so take this opportunity to inhale and exhale deeply several times (five to six deep breaths), bringing a rich supply of oxygen to the lungs and all the other organs of the body. In this position you actually increase your lung's capacity to bring a larger supply of oxygen into your body, so inhale deeply and exhale completely. Try to keep your legs and the lower portion of your body relaxed. To come out of this position raise your head up touch your chin to your chest, relax the elbows and lay down flat on your back. Inhale and exhale deeply as you relax in *The Mummy Pose*.

Opposite above: The pilot fish of Ra: The Barque of Ra.

Bottom: The hieroglyphic symbols for the pilot fish of Ra

Pose 11: The Forward Bend

Left: A yogi performing *The Sitting Forward Bend* - from Ancient Egypt.

1

2

The standing Forward Bend

Pose 11: The Forward Bend

The Sitting Forward Bend is a sitting variation of *The Nut Pose*. It gives gentle massage to all the internal organs of the body such as the kidneys, liver, spleen, and gastro-intestinal system (stomach, intestines and colon) and it stretches the muscles of the body from the foot to the neck and the entire spinal column.

INSTRUCTION:

Come up into a sitting position keeping your back straight (1). Gently rock yourself on your pelvic bone from side to side, and adjust yourself so that you are sitting forward on your pelvic bone. This will allow you to bend forward with ease. Flex your feet so that the bottom of the feet are vertical and flat, as if pushing on an imaginary wall. Let the toes point backwards toward the head. Inhale and raise your arms straight up over your head (2). We'll inhale up and exhale down three times to loosen up. Inhale up, and exhale down, bending forward reaching for your toes. Inhale up and exhale down. Inhale up once more and then exhale down. If you are flexible enough you can actually hold of the bottom of your feet and bring your chest onto your thighs, or place your hands on the floor in front of your feet. If you are not so flexible, reach as far as your can, your ankles, shin, knees, thighs or wherever it is that you feel comfortable, but being sure to keep your back straight. Don't let your back hunch over in the process of stretching forward. More important than how far you can reach forward is that you keep your back straight and breath deeply in this position, inhaling into the areas of tension and then releasing the tension as you exhale, each time reaching forward a little more. To release the posture, exhale and lie down on the mat, slowly and gently, one vertebrae at a time. Relax in *The Mummy Pose.*

Pose 12: The Spinal Twist

1

2

Pose 12: The Spinal Twist

Like the plough, this exercise is very important for the back. Leave one leg extended while you bring the other leg in towards the body by bending the knee while keeping your foot on the floor. Raise one arm and rest it on the bent knee, leaving the other hand behind the body to support yourself. Keep the back straight. Turn the head from side to side. The important thing with this exercise is keeping the back straight. These back exercises help to develop the vertebrae of the spine and they are very important in reviving Osiris or the latent spiritual consciousness within. This is also related to reviving your energy centers of your body. Now turn to the other side and repeat the procedure. Leaving the other leg extended, bring in the other one, leaving one palm facing up towards heaven, and the other facing down towards the earth. The other variation that can be used is to bring one leg and place it on the outside of the other leg that is extended.

Nut, the heavens, is the wife of Geb, the Earth. As his wife, she enfolds him from end to end just as the sky enfolds the planet earth from end to end, from one end of the galaxy to the other. Nut is the mother of all, and within her all human life occurs. Within her is Shu, ether, or space, which separates her from the earth. Above her are the stars. It is also Nut, who conceives Ra every evening. Every evening she consumes him as He sets in the Western horizon and he traverses through her body (the astral plane) and in the morning emerges as Kheper, the new sun.

Meditation: So let us think about ourselves as going up to unite with Nut as we go into the forward bend pose. This position is also known as the inverted position. You should try to touch your heels to the ground by putting one leg forward first, hands in front and raising up moving the leg back. Hold this position and think about Nut who is all encompassing. Her whole body encompasses the entire universe. She extends from one end to the other, and below her is Geb, the earth, the physical nature. Hold this position as long as you like. You may come down, and then raise up once more. Remember to breathe in and out deeply with the belly, concentrating on Nut. Now, come down.

Pose 13: Selket (Serquet) The Scorpion Pose

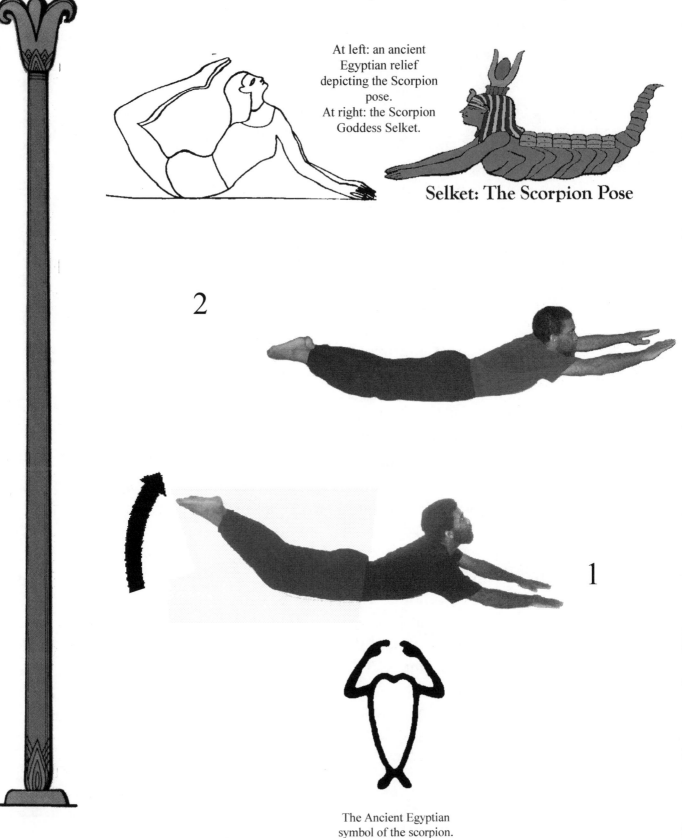

At left: an ancient Egyptian relief depicting the Scorpion pose.
At right: the Scorpion Goddess Selket.

Selket: The Scorpion Pose

2

1

The Ancient Egyptian symbol of the scorpion.

Pose 13: Selket (Serquet) The Scorpion Pose

SELKET, THE SCORPION

Next, raise up slowly to the sitting position, shaking out any tensions. Shake out any tension in the neck, the back, the legs, etc.... Very good. Now we will practice the Selket or Scorpion Pose.

Think about a scorpion's power to inflict pain. Also think about its power of protection. In the story of Isis, Osiris, and Horus, there is a part where after Osiris is killed by Set, Djehuti, or the messenger of wisdom of Ra, the Supreme Being, sends seven scorpions to guard Isis on her journey out of Egypt and away from Set who was trying to kill her and Horus. Mostly, we know of scorpions as evil creatures or hurtful creatures, something like snakes, however, there is another side to all these stories, and once we become aquatinted with the deeper meanings behind the symbolic forms used in myths, we can then begin to discover the inner dimensions of the meditations and exercises.

Now we will proceed to practice the Selket pose. This is the scorpion pose, and in the Indian yoga system, it is known as the locust pose. Lay down on the stomach, forehead touching the ground. Make a fist with the hands, and then place the arms directly under the body. First, we are going to raise the right leg, then the left leg, and then both together. Watch the breath. Breathe in as you raise the leg and breathe out as you let the leg down. Let us begin. Right leg up, right leg down, left leg up, left leg down. Once again, right leg up, right leg down, watching the breath. Tilt head to the side for a few minutes and take a rest. Now raising both legs at the same time, arms underneath the body. Raise up, now down. Raise up, now down. Raise up, now down. Hands at the side, relax. You may hold this position as long as you like. And also raise as high as you like. Greater benefit is derived the higher you raise your legs and the longer you remain in the posture. Remember never to strain or push yourself beyond your limits in any exercise.

Now we will practice a variation on the Selket pose. Position yourself facing forward with your hands in front of you, leaning on your stomach. Now, pushing up and at the same time, raise the legs. Now let them down. Breathe in when you raise the legs, and breathe out when you lower them. Repeat once again. Right away, you will feel that this exercise is good for the muscles in the lower back. Now do this to your capacity. Never Strain. Repeat them one more time. Lie down. Now rest.

Pose 14~ Sebek: The Crocodile Pose

Forms of Sebek

Pose 14~ Sebek: The Crocodile Pose

Sebek is a crocodile god. He assisted Asar in his time of need and he represents the potential power of nature. Specifically, he represents the power that lurks within the waters. He is that power which can rise up at any moment and kill if it is misused and misunderstood or be used for positive goals if sublimated and cultivated.

The crocodile deity is associated with the second psycho-spiritual energy consciousness center.

INSTRUCTION:

1~ Lifting your arms visualize that you are paying homage to the crocodile god himself as you twist your upper body. 2~ Face forward and lower your arms and forehead to the ground before him.

Visualize that you are prostrated before the crocodile god. With bowed head and arms in front of you, bring one knee towards your elbow and then extend it back and bring them together again. Do this exercise for both legs.

Pose 15~ The Cobra Pose

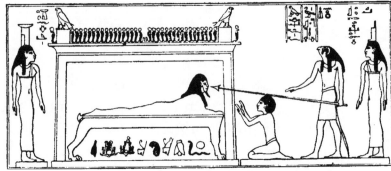

Above: Osiris, resting in the Cobra pose, being resurrected by Horus (From the Temple Resurrection Room.

2

Above: the Cobra

'Netjer Ank'

1

Above: Netjer-Anhk, "The Living God" who gives Life Force which leads to resurrection.

Above: the Goddess Renenet, the bestower of life's fortune according to one's actions

Pose 15~ The Cobra

After a few minutes raise yourself up slowly from the Sebek posture to the sitting position, shaking out any tensions. Shake out any tension in the neck, the back, the legs, etc.... Very good.

Now we will practice the Cobra, serpent or Uraeus pose. The Uraeus is a goddess, equivalent to the Indian Kundalini. The serpent power is related to the energy centers of the body and is also intimately related to the resurrection of Osiris. It is related specifically to the vertebrae and the back of the yoga practitioner, thus in raising the power of the back, the spiritual Life Force and consciousness is raised. One is raising Osiris within one's self. Therefore, the Uraeus exercise and the scorpion exercise are strongly related to the spiritual development of the energy centers of the body. When the latent Life Force psycho-spiritual energy reaches the level of the

Nehebkau.

sixth energy center at the forehead, there dawns intuitional vision of the Self. This is symbolized by the Cobra worn at the forehead in ancient Egyptian masks, crowns, etc.

Now, lay on your stomach, with your hands under your shoulders, and your forehead touching the ground. Breathing in, raise the chest off the ground, without pushing with your arms and release down, breathing out, forehead to the ground. Repeat two more times. Now move up. Now move down. Repeat one more time. Now rest for a moment. This time, push up with the hands, gently, and to your capacity, keeping the elbows close to the sides of the body. Now, release and lower your forehead back to the ground, breathing out., Perform the Cobra once more. Push up as high as you can, holding as long as you like. Now relax.

The Serpent Goddess of ancient Egypt.

Pose 16– Sphinx: The Horemakhet Pose

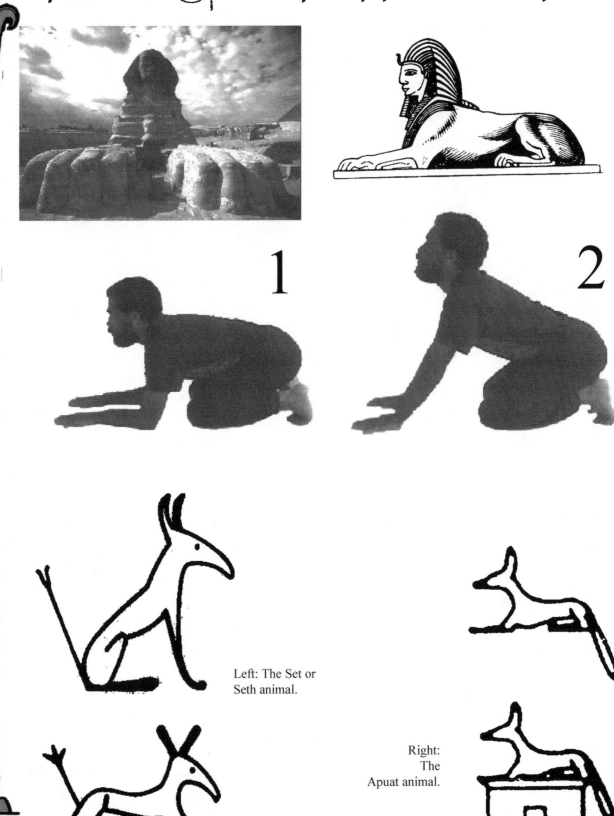

1

2

Left: The Set or
Seth animal.

Right:
The
Apuat animal.

Pose 16~ Sphinx: The Horemakhet Pose

The Next posture we will practice is the Sphinx. It is related to the deity Apuat (Anus) and Set. The Sphinx is the most Ancient Egyptian symbol known. It represents several important mystical principles. Foremost among these is the ideal of a human being who has reached the heights of enlightenment while controlling the lower self at the same time. Therefore, as you practice this posture see yourself as a Sphinx. Visualize that you are the mind, the spirit and that your body is as powerful as that of a lion. See yourself as the perfect combination of body and soul.

INSTRUCTION:

First rest on your heels. Then lean forward and place your hands in front of you. Rest on your elbows. This is the recumbent phase of the posture. Now raise up the front of your body by pushing up from your elbows. This is the extended phase of the posture. Feel the stretch in your back.

Pose 17~ The Heru Pose

As stated earlier, Heru is the defender. He represents spiritual aspiration and will power to back up that aspiration to overcome unrighteousness, ignorance and even death.

He assisted in the resurrection of his father and through his warrior skills defeated Set, the agent of ignorance and freed the land from injustice.

Below: Horus as the Hawk from the Temple at Ombos, Nubia, Africa.

Above: Heru khuti: Heru of the two Horizons, the all encompassing one.

Horus as the Hawk, holding the Uas scepter (flow of energy to Creation.

From the tomb of King Tutankhamun.

Heru as king of Egypt

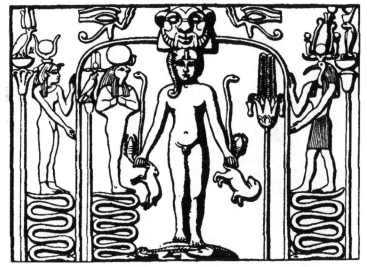

Above: Heru as a Divine child, master of nature, controller of beasts (evil, unrighteousness, the lower self).

THE POSTURE

Come to a standing posture, remaining motionless and see yourself as a powerful, immovable mountain, a pyramid, etc. See yourself as a righteous warrior, protector of the weak, upstanding and true. Visualize yourself as that redeemer of your own soul, the leader of your own destiny, the protector of your own life, the architect of your own destiny.

As you commence the next phase of the program, visualize yourself as bringing all of the qualities of Heru into your practice.

Visualize that the power and wisdom of your self-discovery in the lower self (beginning through the Transition Phase) will be transformed into the glorious self-discovery of the Higher Self which is to follow now.

Above: Heru Behdet: The warrior, defender of truth and restorer of righteousness.

Pose 18~ Anpu: The Henu Pose

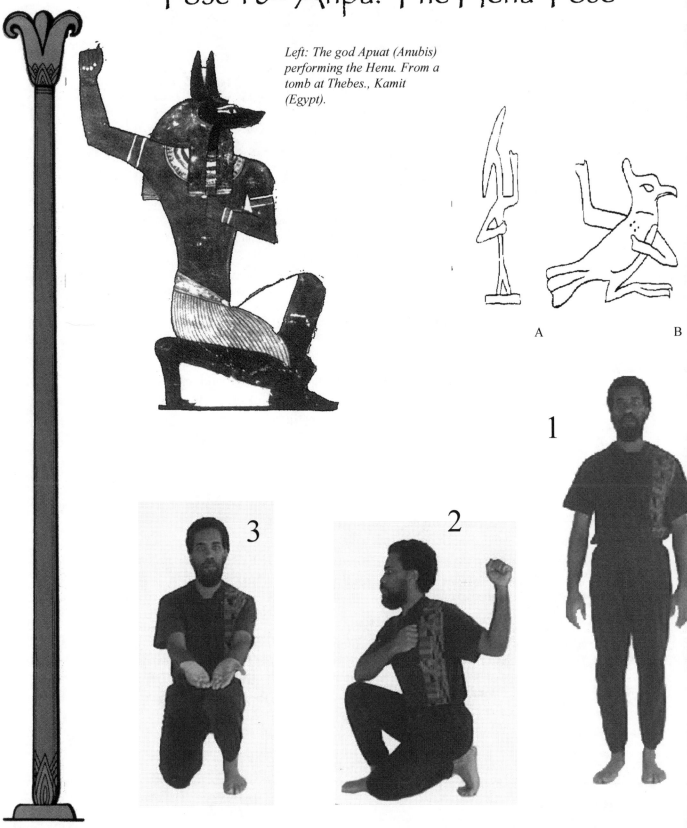

Left: The god Apuat (Anubis) performing the Henu. From a tomb at Thebes., Kamit (Egypt).

A

B

1

2

3

Pose 18~ Anpu: The Henu Pose

Opposite: *A- Jubilating Was scepter from the relief of Djoser.*

B- Jubilating Rekhyt bird. Scene from the relief of Amenemhet I. The Rekhyt bird symbolizes "The People of Egypt".

In the **HENU** exercise (Figures A and B Left), prayers are offered to the Divine Self, God.

Henu symbolizes "praise", "rejoicing" and "jubilation". There are many hieroglyphic reliefs showing Gods as well as initiates performing the Henu exercise. First one kneels on one knee and extends one arm with palm open while at the same time holding the other arm closer to the body with closed fist. Then the extended arm is drawn back and the hand is closed as it touches the chest. The performance is repeated several times and ends with the final position where one arm is raised behind the head with closed fist and the other arm touches the chest with closed fist.

Pose 19 – Nut: The Inverted Pose

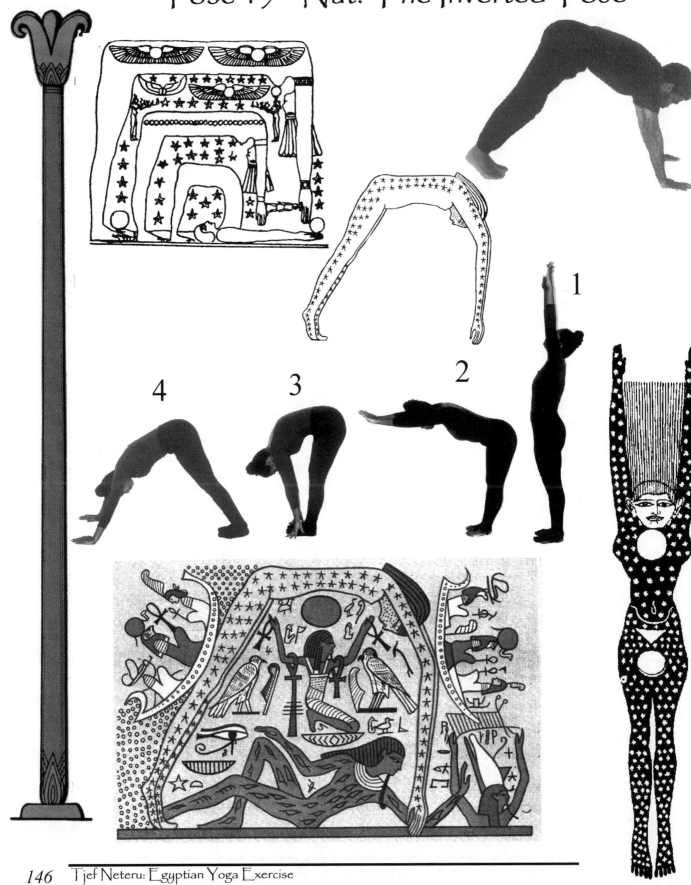

1

2

3

4

Pose 19– Nut: The Inverted Pose

Now we will practice the Nut pose. You will recall that we introduced goddess Nut earlier as the heavens and as the mother of Aset. Also, we practiced the sitting forward bend. Now we will practice the exercise with a different emphasis. This posture is to be practiced in the standing position and with the special visualization of Nut.

INSTRUCTION:

Stand straight and stretch out your arms directly above your head. Stretch the right side and then the left. Now bow down while keeping the arms in line with the upper body and touch the ground beside your feet if you can or grab your ankles. If you need to bend your knees in order to reach down.

Now keep your feet in the same position while you walk your hands forwards in front of you and make a mountain with your body. Stretch yourself as Nut does. Close your eyes and visualize that you are encompassing the entire earth.

Come out of the position by reversing the instructions just given.

Above: The Nut extended posture on the tips of the fingers and the toes.

Pose 20~ The Maat Pose

Above: The Goddess Maat presides over the balance of the heart of the spiritual initiate.

1

2

3

4

5

Above: The Goddess Maat performing the Maat pose in the Tomb of Nefertari, Egypt, Africa.

Left: Goddess Maat with the papyrus scepter and Ankh.

Pose 20~ The Maat Pose

On the opposite page you can see a picture of Maat. Maat is a daughter of Ra. It is said that Maat is the foundation of creation. Ra stands in his boat of creation on the pedestal of Maat. So what is Maat? Maat is order, righteousness, justice, truth. Maat also implies a righteous way of life based on order, duty, dispassion and cosmic awareness. There is a very deep philosophy behind Maat. You can look at our Philosophy video in order to get more on this as well as the books *Egyptian Yoga: The Philosophy of Enlightenment* and *Egyptian Proverbs*. Essentially, what you need to think about as you perform the exercise is becoming like Maat, becoming truthful, becoming righteous, becoming orderly within yourself. What does that mean? That means understanding your oneness with the universe, understanding that you are the daughter or the son of the Supreme Being. You must understand that you are immortal, eternal and essentially one with the Divine. You are not just a mortal individual caught in a world of time and space. You are the master of the universe as you exist by Maat.

INSTRUCTIONS:

With legs two feet apart, raise both arms as if you are unfurling your spiritual wings. Turn the head to the side, twisting the leg, now kneel down. Breathing in and come up, turn to the other side. See yourself as having wings to fly on. When you are truthful and righteous, you become at peace. When you are at peace, you can fly, your thoughts can fly, your ideas can fly. When you are in tension, you are constricted and agitated. Your mind, your thoughts cannot fly. Your spirit becomes trapped in the body and has no awareness of the greater world that exists beyond the body. Arms down and rest. Breathing in and out. OM. peace.

Spread your legs apart about two feet and what we do basically is that as you Maat represents truth justice and righteousness. Maat is the very foundation of creation it is the basis of everything it is the basis for you of me, of everything, it is the basis of being able to come into harmony with all those around us. When we act in ways that are harmonious with Maat when we act in truthful righteous and just ways then we come into harmony with Maat. Keep these in mind as we do the posture. You can lower your arms right now cause let me just say one more thing as you inhale and unfurl your wings of Maat what I want you to do is to focus and if you have seen the pictures of the balance of the scales of Maat from your right hand see that the scale is hanging off of it and that scale see your heart and on the left hand see the feather of Maat so as you do the posture you will have your ab or your heart on the scale in your right hand and you will have the feather of Maat on your left hand on the scale and try to keep the balance try to keep your heart as light as the feather of Maat. Spread your legs apart and then go ahead and we are going to twist our feet to the right and bring your head to the right so we are basically looking forward at our hand and lower yourself to the ground, lower the left knee onto the ground and go back sit on our heel the left heel and then we can bring our heel all the way down and sit on our foot try to maintain the balance and then inhale we come up and turn back facing forward exhale release the arms and shake the arms out a little bit inhale up and furl the wings of Maat turn to the left feet to the left face our left arm the feathers of Maat and lower ourselves to the ground bring our right knee onto the ground sit on our right heel and then we can point our toes and sit all the way down on the right foot try to keep the balance and inhale up slowly and gently and turn forward and release the arms and shake out the arms. relax and shake out the arms when you feel a pain in your thighs tomorrow yes, think of Maat.

Pose 21~ The Aset Victory Pose

The forms of Isis

Pose 21~ The Aset Victory Pose

Now the Isis Pose. Maat and Isis are related to each other. Both represent order, justice, wisdom and truth. These qualities are essential on the spiritual path. Therefore, while practicing the Isis pose, there should be a keen understanding of the qualities embodied in Isis. There is no better way to do this except by visualizing yourself as being imbued with those qualities by seeing yourself as Isis.

Think of yourself as Isis. As we said earlier, Isis is the daughter of Nut and Geb, and wife of Osiris. Isis is the embodiment of wisdom, not just intellectual knowledge, but spiritual knowledge which comes from experiencing the transcendental realms of existence. This is real knowledge which cannot come from books or any intellectual exercise of the mind. Isis is the one who comes and saves Osiris after he was killed by Set.

INSTRUCTION:

Place the right leg in front, raise arms to the side and exhaling, come down. Inhale and come up. Come to the original position, watching the breath. Now place the left leg to the front, arms out to the side up, going down, breathing in coming up, breathing out going down. Repeat one more time.

Pose 22- The Aset Throne Pose

The Goddess Aset
(Isis) sitting on the
throne,
suckling Heru.

The practice of the Throne-
Sitting Posture

The God Asar sitting on
the throne of Aset (Isis).
The goddesses Aset and
Nebthet (Nephthys)
stand behind the throne.

The Goddess Net (Aset-
Isis) sitting on the throne.

The Goddess Hetheru
sitting on the throne.

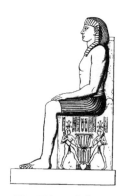

The King sitting on
the throne of Aset.

Pose 22~ The Aset Throne Pose

Asar

Aset

The goddess, who symbolizes creation itself, the physical universe, supports the incarnation of the soul (Asar). In this way, the physical (Aset) supports the spirit (Asar). This is why the symbol of the throne is used in the name of the god Asar and the goddess Aset. This symbol of the goddess herself is the throne, and this is why the throne seat, ▯, is where Asar is shown seated. The name Asar is spelled with the throne symbol, the eye symbol, ☞. And the male determinative, ⚱. The eye symbol written in this manner means "to make," "create," "to do" or "engender." Therefore, the mystical symbolism of the name Asar is the essence, which procreates or comes into existence through Aset.

The symbols of the name of Aset are the throne seat, ▯ "as", the phonetic sign for "t", ◡, the determinative egg, ◯ , symbol of motherhood, and the female determinative, ⚱ .

This manner of reading of the name of Asar is supported by the myth of Asar and Aset as well as their epithets and their iconographies. The name Asar is intimately related to the name Aset. Asar and Aset are often referred to as "brother" and "sister." This relates to the idea that they come from the same parent, i.e. the same spiritual source. In ancient times men and women who married were also referred to as brother and sister. This had no relation to their parentage. Rather, this epithet relates to the mystical origins of all human beings. Essentially, we are all brothers and sisters. As our true nature is not man and woman but soul, and our parent, the Universal Spirit.

Through the myth of the Asarian Resurrection, we learn that Asar and Aset are Avatars, divine incarnations, sent to earth to lead souls, incarnating as human beings, towards righteousness, prosperity and spiritual enlightenment. In a higher sense, Asar represents the soul of every human being which comes to earth and must struggle to overcome the lower nature, who is symbolized by Set.

Instruction:

Raise the arms with palms facing downward. Bending the knees, lower yourself as far as you can comfortably go as if you were to sit on the throne of the goddess. Visualize yourself as being supported by the beneficent power of the goddess, who is the great and compassionate mother. Stay in the posture for as long as is comfortable, raise yourself up and repeat once more.

Pose 23- Hept: The Aset Embrace Pose

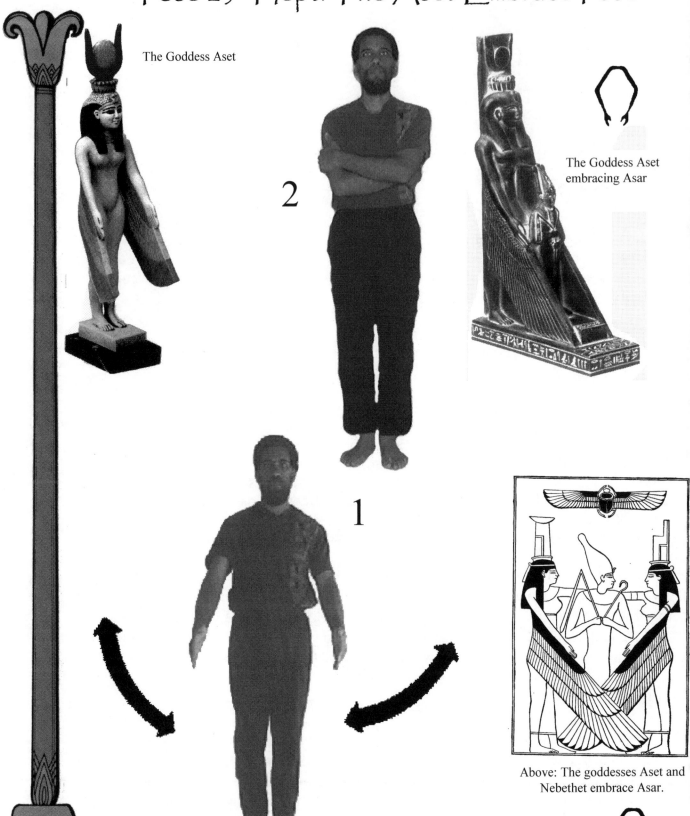

The Goddess Aset

2

1

The Goddess Aset
embracing Asar

Above: The goddesses Aset and
Nebethet embrace Asar.

Pose 23- Hept: The Aset Embrace Pose

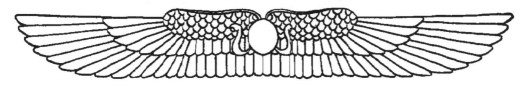

Above: The all-embracing, all-encompassing wings of Heru.

The Embrace Posture, refers to the act of hugging or embracing. The goddess Aset is the quintessential ideal of the idea behind this pose. She embraced Asar and Heru in their time of need and brought them back to life. In the same way, a spiritual aspirant should understand that the Aset quality within them is capable of encompassing their entire life in order to resurrect it from the grips of dullness, negativity and misery.

Thus, visualize yourself as a gigantic image of Aset and see yourself embracing your body, your very personality.

You are Asar and Aset has come to enfold you with the love and peace which she brings to resurrect you.

INSTRUCTION:

Wave your arms from side to side and with your eyes closed see yourself embracing the entire world. There are no good or bad things in the world, only the embrace which encompasses all. Allow Aset within you to emerge with the power of all encompassing devotion, compassion and love for all.

Pose 24~ Djed: Established in Asar Pose

The Mystical Implications of the Djed

The *Djed* pillar, ⚊, is associated with the Ancient Egyptian Gods, Ptah as well as Osiris. It is part of a profound mystical teaching that encompasses the mystical Life Force energy which engenders the universe and which is the driving force that sustains all life and impels human beings to action. In the Ausarian Resurrection myth it is written that when Osiris was killed by Set, his body was thrown into the Nile and it came ashore on the banks of Syria. There it grew into a tree with a fragrant aroma and the king of that land had it cut into a pillar. The pillar of Osiris-Ptah refers to the human vertebrae and the Serpent Power or Life Force energy which exists in the subtle spine of every human being. It refers to the four highest states of psycho-spiritual consciousness in a human being with the uppermost tier symbolizing ultimate spiritual enlightenment. Also, the Djed refers to the special realm of the Duat (astral Plane) wherein Osiris or spiritual resurrection can be discovered in much the same way as the Christian *Tree of Life* refers to resurrection in Christian mystical mythology.

The Duat or Ancient Egyptian concept of the *Netherworld* is a special place of existence. This is the abode of Osiris-Ptah as well as the ultimate destination of those who become spiritually enlightened. It is the realm of Supreme Peace. It is known as *Sekhet-Aaru* or in other times *Amentet*. Amentet is a reference which unites the symbolism of Osiris and Ptah with that of Amun, thus relating the deities of Ancient Egypt into a singular essence and dispelling the notion of polytheism. This is an important Tantric theme. The Djed symbolizes the awakening human soul who is well "established" or "steadfast" or "stability" in the knowledge of the

Self. *Djeddu,* , refers to the abode of Osiris within the Duat.

Djeddu was the name of two towns in Ancient Egypt. In mystical terms it refers to being firmly established in the Netherworld. The Ancient Egyptian word Djeddu also refers to "steadfastness" or "stability" as well as the pillar of Osiris. This is the principle being referred to in the following verse from the *Egyptian Book of Coming Forth By Day*, Chapter I: 13-15:

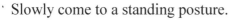
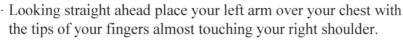

nuk Djeddy, se Djeddy au am-a em Djeddu Mesi - a em Djeddu

"I am Djeddy (steadfast), son of Djeddy (steadfast), conceived and born in the region of Djeddu (steadfastness)."

PRACTICING THE POSTURE

· Slowly come to a standing posture.

· Looking straight ahead place your left arm over your chest with the tips of your fingers almost touching your right shoulder.

Now bend your right arm and cross your chest over your left arm and touch your chest.

Now find a comfortable position and remain completely motionless, being as if encased in an impregnable pillar.

Visualize that you are established in the teaching, that you are firm in your resolution and will to act, think, feel and bee one in divine consciousness with Creation and the spirit.

Visualize that your are the conduit between heaven and earth and that you are immovable

Pose 25- The Headstand Pose

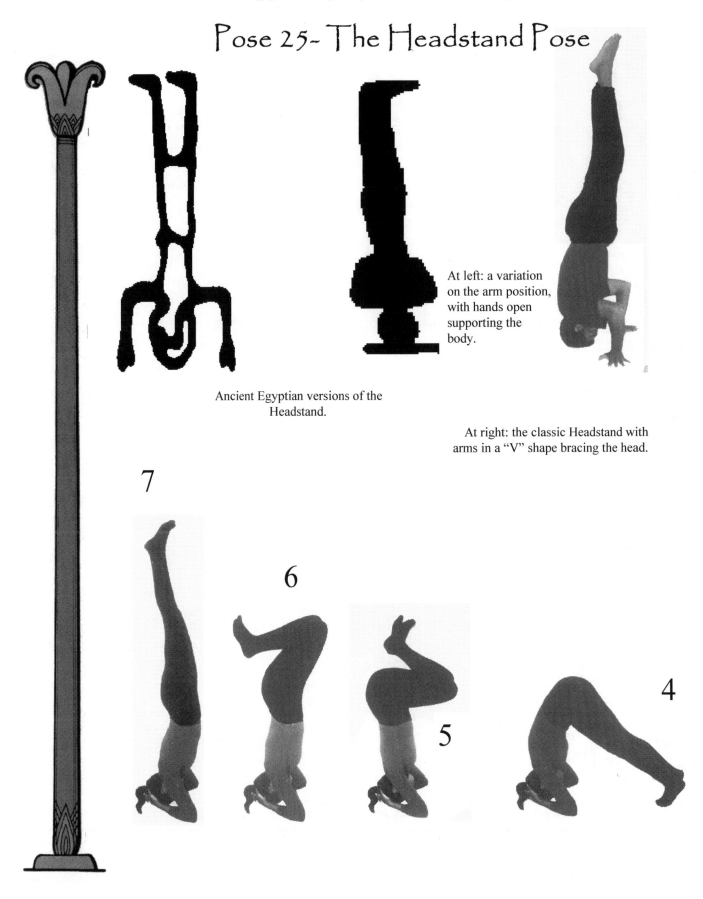

At left: a variation on the arm position, with hands open supporting the body.

Ancient Egyptian versions of the Headstand.

At right: the classic Headstand with arms in a "V" shape bracing the head.

7

6

5

4

Pose 25- The Headstand Pose

THE HEAD STAND

Now we are going to practice the head stand. This is one of the more difficult postures of yoga. If you find that you cannot do it without support, go close to a wall to support you as you raise your legs. Measure one forearm's length to measure the distance to use for your "V" shape support at the elbows and interlock your fingers. Now place the hands behind the head, making a "V" with the elbows. Walking into position, bring the legs closer to the body and slowly move the lower portion of the body up. Once you are up, you may practice variations, such as moving legs from side to side if you feel you can.

Hold as long as you can. To come down, move the body following the steps above in reverse order. Bring legs close to the body, then down to the ground. Lay flat on your back to equalize the pressure and allow the blood to flow normally again.

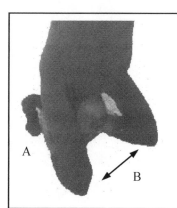

Fig. 33B

The "V" shape elbow position for the head stand.
Interlock the fingers and cup the back of the head with the hands (A). Move the elbows apart by the distance of one forearm's length (B).

3

2

1

Above: the sequence for practicing the Headstand. The center photo shows the arms in a "V" shape with hands interlocked and bracing the head. The left and right pictures show a more difficult variation with palms open.

Pose 26~ Khepri: The Scarab Pose

Khepri, the morning sun.   Rā, the noon-   Temu (Atem), the
                             day sun.   setting sun.

Rā, the god One or Only god, in his three chief aspects.

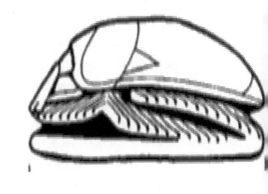

Khepri in his boat.

Pose 26~ Khepri: The Scarab Pose

Now squat on the floor with your forehead on the ground and the knees tucked into the chest . This is the pose of transformation, the Scarab. You are taking all the benefits from the exercises and keeping them within the body. Think of yourself as a scarab. You are transforming yourself mentally, physically, and spiritually.

The beetle is a very important pose. The scarab (dung beetle of Egypt) is an insect which burrows into the mud caused by the Nile flood waters, and after the muddy waters recede, the beetle comes up with a new body, a new being. The beetle is likened to Ra, the sun, in the morning who comes out of the murky waters of the dark night. The sun rises in the morning as a new being. The scarab (energy of transformation) pushes the sun on its journey every day. In the morning, the sun is Kheper, the scarab, at noon it becomes Ra, and in the evening, the setting sun, it is Tem. These different phases, symbolize the one Supreme Being which manifests as a triad of time, past, present and future.

The scarab symbolizes transformation, and here we are transforming ourselves mentally, physically and spiritually into higher beings, higher beings. Let go of all the tension and mental agitation. In letting go, we are transforming our selves, we are becoming peaceful, we are becoming true agents of Hetep and coming into harmony with Maat.

Mediate on this for a minute, watching the breath.

Pose 27~ Asar: The Mummy or Corpse Pose and Meditation

 The Ancient Egyptian Hieroglyph of the Corpse

Now, let us practice the final exercise. This exercise is going to be always preceded by the scarab, and all these exercises that have been given. This exercise is a meditative posture as well. All the benefits that we derived from our exercises, meditations, postures and mental exercises that we have done in this period, we are going to bring them into this posture and allow them to integrate into our personalities and become part of us.

Now, as we said before, Osiris was killed by Set who was jealous of him. Isis came to revive him and resurrect him. This is the Great Resurrection that Isis performed for Osiris the true meaning behind the corpse pose or mummy pose. By allowing the wisdom of Isis to become part of you, you will be resurrected from your state of ignorance into the state of supreme wisdom to experience your true divine nature and discover your immortality.

Isis addressing the mummy of Osiris as it lay in her boat ready for removal to the tomb.

Pose 27 – Asar: The Mummy or Corpse Pose and Meditation

Osiris standing between Isis and Nephthys.
From a bas-relief at Philae.

Lay flat on your back, legs two feet apart, arms one foot away from the body, watching the breath.

Visualize the ancient relief of Isis hovering over Osiris. Keep your body perfectly still. Visualize it as being dead. Visualize it as being life-less. Now picture the form of Isis. Her magnificent wing shape, hovering about you flying back and forth. Now she is coming closer and closer to your lifeless body. Now you can feel the air, the wind, being blown from her wings as she hovers directly above you. Feel the wind, not just blowing on the body but blowing through it. Visualize her wings encompassing the whole world and you are the whole world. Visualize her wings enfolding you. They are unfurling and unfolding. Visualize Isis coming directly over you and on top of you. Feel that you are completely enfolded by her wings. Feel her love, compassion and majesty. She is beautiful and wise. Look into her eyes, dark and mysterious, see the depth of her being. She is transcendental, from her golden arms the multicolored wings emerge. Her wings span the entire universe and yet she is here with you. Isis is touching you. She is one with you now. Now feel the vitality, the energy of the entire universe coming into you. Feel yourself as being one with all that exists. This is Isis. This is the wisdom that she brings. You are not the body, but the spirit energy that resides in the body, you are Isis. Let Isis live through you. Let Isis become one with you. Visualize your arms and see wings sprouting from your arms. See the wings unfurling. Now see yourself coming up from the body; you are being resurrected. Fly up, up, up, through the roof, through the air, above the clouds. Rise above the clouds of your thoughts and your mind. There is no contradiction; there is total oneness.

Look at the sun. Now fly towards it. Feel its rays. They are not hot. They are cool; they are soothing. Fly to the sun, embrace it. Be-

Pose 27- Asar: The Mummy or Corpse Pose and Meditation

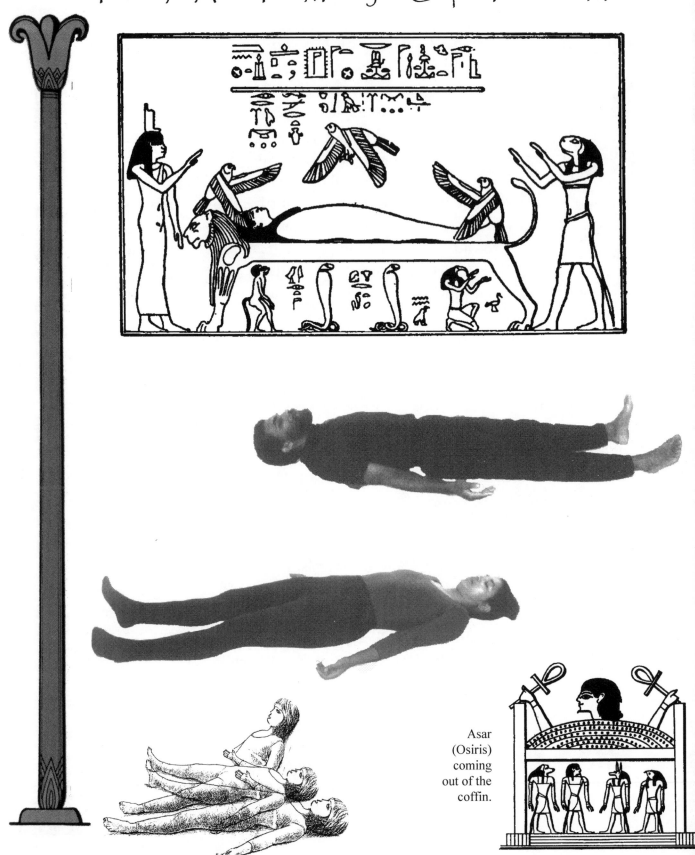

Asar (Osiris) coming out of the coffin.

Pose 27 – Asar: The Mummy or Corpse Pose and Meditation

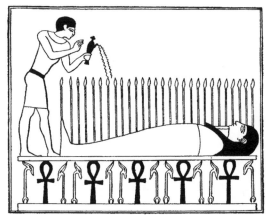

Osiris-Neprà, with wheat growing from his body.
From a bas-relief at Philae.

The soul of the scribe Nebseni visiting its mummified body in the tomb.

come one with it. The sun is the Supreme Being; it is Ra, not the physical sun, but the spiritual principle behind it, the light of consciousness itself. Now look at the moon and fly towards it. It is Isis, that is also you. Embrace it, become one with it. Now, look at your eyes. Look at your body there. Look at the eyes and visualize the eye of Horus and the eye of Ra in place of your eyes. You are one with the universe. You encompass all things and you have knowledge of your true Self, your spiritual Self. You have the eye of Ra and you have the eye of Horus within you and this is the legacy of the Neters. This is your legacy. Meditate on this for a minute, watching the breath.

Stay here now in silence for as long as you like.

Now, coming back to body consciousness, gradually move your toes, ankles, knees, hips, stomach, chest, arms and shoulders, neck side to side. Om. Peace.

Now, if you would like to you may go ahead, while you are in this transcendental mood, with your body fully exercised, the energies balanced, and the forces within your spiritual self, to heal yourself or practice meditation. If you want to do some healing now, visualize

Pose 27– Asar: The Mummy or Corpse Pose and Meditation

any part of the body that needs healing and direct the energies (the Prana, the chi, the sekhem, Life Force) there for a few seconds. Direct it to the part of the body that is in need of assistance.

We have already practiced mediation through out this program today, but if you would like to do a formal meditation, this would be the best time to do it. Now that your mind and body and spirit are energized, yet relaxed. If not, you may go through the day always trying to keep a peaceful mind. Always try to understand that the obstacles you are going through in life are all for your benefit. They are all challenges for you to exert your will, for you to develop your spiritual strength and hold on to your spiritual peace, and your spiritual knowledge. If you are challenged by those who are ignorant, those who are trying to hurt you, don't become one with their level. Always try to remember who "you" are. Remember Maat. Remember that your strength is derived from Isis, and is not from any possession or relationship that you have; it is derived from Isis. Everything is given light through Isis, through the Supreme Being, so therefore, if there is anything in your life that gives you pleasure it is because of the Supreme Being, who is present there. So do not become attached to objects but to the spiritual principle which flows through them and all creation. So don't look at the object itself as a source of pain or pleasure, look at the spiritual basis of the object. Everything in the universe is part of that supreme ocean that we spoke of in the beginning, and that ocean is nothing but the Supreme Being. May you attain wisdom, may you travel in peace, may you travel in justice and righteousness and honor and love.

Peace be with you.

Questions for reflection and study

Purification of the Body - Physical Exercise Practice Questions.

1- What is the importance of getting proper sleep?

_____
_____
_____
_____
_____
_____

2- What is the importance of proper breathing?

_____
_____
_____
_____
_____

3- Describe the process of proper breathing.

_____
_____
_____
_____
_____

4- What is the most important purpose of physical exercise?

_____
_____
_____
_____
_____

5- What happens to the inner vital forces of the body when yoga ex-

Questions for reflection and study

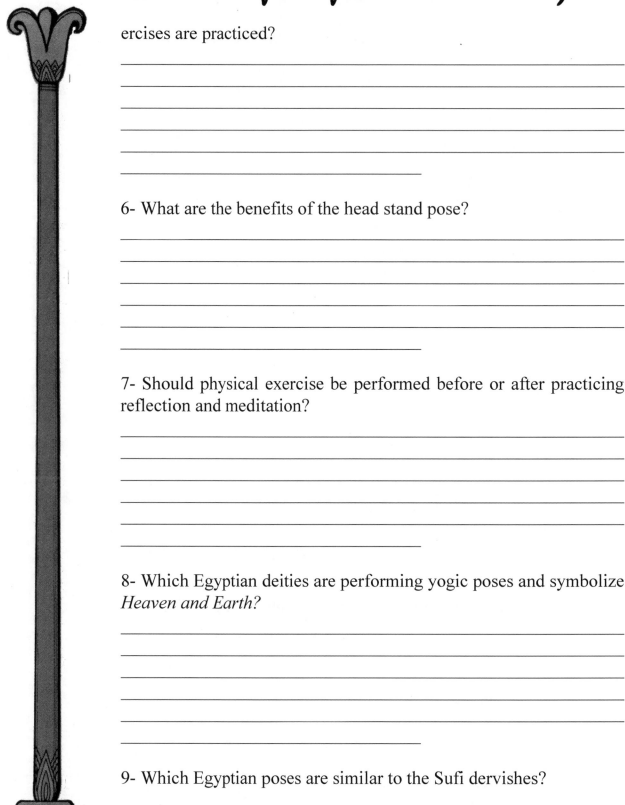

ercises are practiced?

_____

_____

_____

_____

_____

_____

6- What are the benefits of the head stand pose?

_____

_____

_____

_____

_____

_____

7- Should physical exercise be performed before or after practicing reflection and meditation?

_____

_____

_____

_____

_____

_____

8- Which Egyptian deities are performing yogic poses and symbolize *Heaven and Earth?*

_____

_____

_____

_____

_____

_____

9- Which Egyptian poses are similar to the Sufi dervishes?

Questions for reflection and study

_____
_____
_____
_____
_____
_____

10- What is the exercise pose being performed by the deities *Shu, Nut and Geb?*

_____
_____
_____
_____
_____
_____

11- Turning to the video (which accompanies this lesson), follow the sequence of the exercises and then note in writing your experiences.

_____
_____
_____
_____

12- What is the breathing exercise which emphasizes harmonizing the energies of the body?

_____

Questions for reflection and study

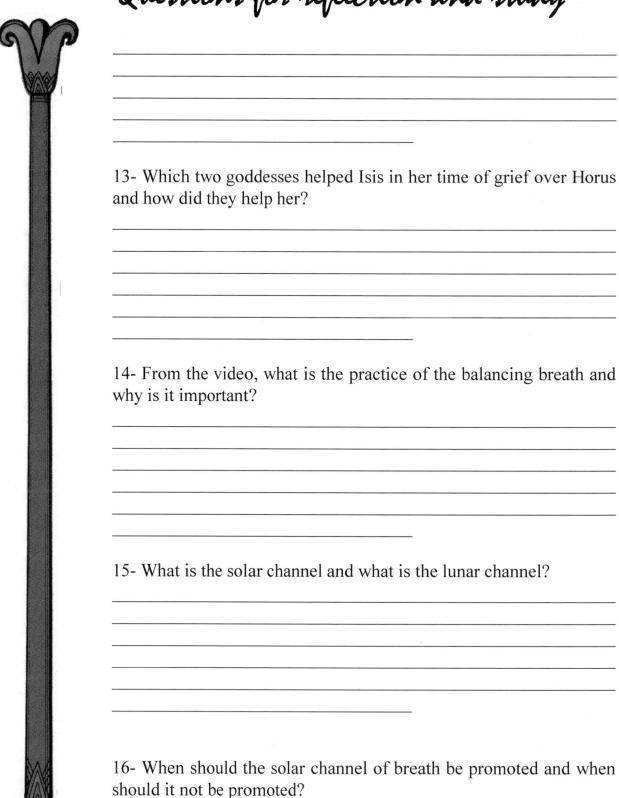

13- Which two goddesses helped Isis in her time of grief over Horus and how did they help her?

14- From the video, what is the practice of the balancing breath and why is it important?

15- What is the solar channel and what is the lunar channel?

16- When should the solar channel of breath be promoted and when should it not be promoted?

Questions for reflection and study

_____

_____

_____

_____

_____

_____

17- When should the balancing breath exercise be practiced?

_____

_____

_____

_____

_____

18- Which deity(s) preside(s) over the subtle channels of the internal Life Force energy?

_____

_____

_____

_____

_____

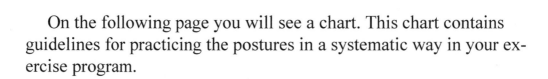

Working with the postures of Egyptian Yoga

On the following page you will see a chart. This chart contains guidelines for practicing the postures in a systematic way in your exercise program.

In the beginning you should practice the basic program. As you progress you may add additional postures to your program. To increase the intensity of your workout you can also practice more repetitions of each posture.

In order to gain the meditative benefits of the postures you can follow the guidelines given in the Meditative Series column.

You should attempt to perform the basic program daily. As you progress you may perform the medium program daily and as you progress further you can perform the Intensive program and the meditative programs.

There are two ways to increase the intensity of the programs. One way is to increase the repetitions performed. This will provide the benefit of physical health and vitality.

The second way to increase the intensity of the workout is to increase the hold time of each posture, the time you stay in it. This practice is used in the meditative workout. It will bring increased stamina and will power. For more on the meditative workout follow the program in the audio session. Tape #603 Egyptian Yoga Exercise Workout Level Three.

Egyptian Yoga Exercise Program Guidelines

	POSTURE	Beginner Session	BASIC Session	MEDIUM Session	MEDITATIVE Session
1	Karast (Mummy) Pose	2 minutes	2 minutes	5 minutes	5 minutes
2	Nefertem Lotus Pose	2 minutes	5 minutes	10 minutes	10 minutes
3	Nun Pose.	2 reps*	3 reps*	4 reps*	2 reps*
4	Warm Up	1 minute	2 minutes	5 minutes	2 minutes
5	Shu Pose	2 reps*	3 reps*	4 reps*	2 reps*
6	Journey of Ra Pose Series	1 set*	1 set*	4-6 reps*	1 set hold each posture 30 seconds
7	Shoulder-stand Pose, Plough Pose,		1 rep*	2 reps*	1 rep*
8	Wheel Pose,		1 rep*	2 reps*	1 rep*
9	Fish Pose		1 rep*	1 reps*	1 rep*
10	Spinal Twist Pose	1 rep*	2 rep*	3 reps*	1 rep*
11	Forward Bend Pose and	2 reps*	2 reps*	3 reps*	2 reps*
12	Selket –Scorpion Pose		2 reps*	4 reps*	2 reps*
13	Sebek –Crocodile Pose	2 reps*	2 reps*	4 reps*	2 reps*
14	Arat- Cobra Pose	2 reps*	2 reps*	3 reps*	2 reps*
15	Horemacket –Sphinx Pose	1 rep*	2 rep*	4 reps*	1 rep*
16	Heru – Horus Pose and variations	1 rep*	1 rep*	1 rep*	1 rep*
17	Henu Pose		2 sets*	2 reps*	2 sets*
18	Nut Pose	1 rep*	1 rep*	2 reps*	1 rep*
19	Maat Pose	1 set*	1 set*	2 reps*	1 set*
20	Aset Pose	1 set*	1 set*	2 reps*	1 set*
21	Aset Sitting Pose	2 reps*	3 reps*	4 reps*	2 reps*
22	Aset Embrace Pose	2 reps*	2 reps*	4 reps*	2 reps*
23	Djed Pose	1 rep*	1 rep*	1 rep*	1 rep*
24	Headstand Pose		1 rep*	1 rep*	1 rep*
25	Khepri— Scarab Pose	1 minute	3 minutes	5 minutes	5 minutes
26	Shti (Mummy) Pose	3 minutes	5 minutes	10 minutes	15 minutes
		*hold for 30 seconds	*hold for one minute	*hold for one minute	*hold for three to five minutes or as long as you can.

Egyptian Yoga Exercise Video Series

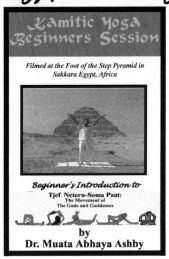

Available as DVD $10.00

Available as DVD $10.00

AUDIO CASSETTE EXERCISE SERIES
600 WC The Egyptian Yoga Exercise Workout with Vijaya Level I short session $9.99 45 min.
601 WC The Egyptian Yoga Exercise Workout with Vijaya Level II long session $9.99 - 90min
603 WC The Egyptian Yoga Exercise Workout with Muata Level III - long session $9.99 - 90min

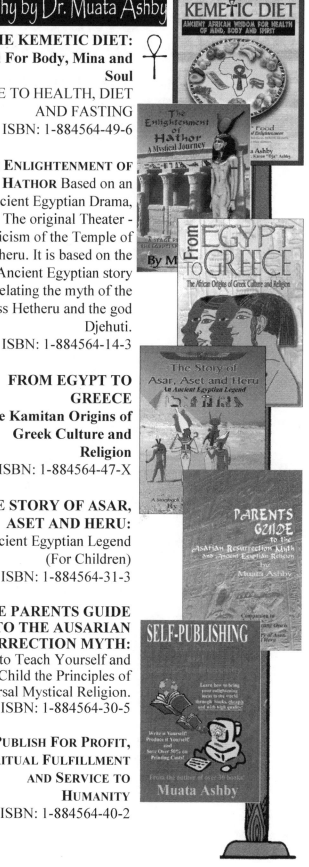

Egyptian Yoga and Kemetic Philosophy by Dr. Muata Ashby

AFRICAN ORIGINS OF CIVILIZATION, MYSTICAL RELIGION AND YOGA PHILOSOPHY (Hard Cover First Edition) ISBN: 1-884564-50-X

AFRICAN ORIGINS BOOK 1 PART 1 African Origins of African Civilization, Religion, Yoga Mysticism and Ethics PhilosophyISBN: 1-884564-55-0 (Soft)

AFRICAN ORIGINS BOOK 2 PART 2 African Origins of Western Civilization, Religion and Philosophy (Soft) ISBN: 1-884564-56-9

AFRICAN ORIGINS BOOK 3 PART 3 African Origins of Eastern Civilization, Religion, Yoga Mysticism and Philosophy(Soft) ISBN: 1-884564-57-7

HEALING THE CRIMINAL HEART Ancient Egyptian Psychology to redeem the Soul ISBN: 1-884564-17-8

THE KING OF EGYPT: The Struggle of Good and Evil for Control of the World and The Human Soul ISBN 1-8840564-44-5

THE MYSTERIES OF ISIS The Path of Wisdom, Immortality and Enlightenment ISBN 1-884564-24-0

THE KEMETIC DIET: Food For Body, Mina and Soul GUIDE TO HEALTH, DIET AND FASTING ISBN: 1-884564-49-6

THE ENLIGHTENMENT OF HATHOR Based on an Ancient Egyptian Drama, The original Theater - Mysticism of the Temple of Hetheru. It is based on the Ancient Egyptian story relating the myth of the goddess Hetheru and the god Djehuti. ISBN: 1-884564-14-3

FROM EGYPT TO GREECE The Kamitan Origins of Greek Culture and Religion ISBN: 1-884564-47-X

THE STORY OF ASAR, ASET AND HERU: An Ancient Egyptian Legend (For Children) ISBN: 1-884564-31-3

THE PARENTS GUIDE TO THE AUSARIAN RESURRECTION MYTH: How to Teach Yourself and Your Child the Principles of Universal Mystical Religion. ISBN: 1-884564-30-5

SELF-PUBLISH FOR PROFIT, SPIRITUAL FULFILLMENT AND SERVICE TO HUMANITY ISBN: 1-884564-40-2

OTHER BOOKS BY MUATA ASHBY

EGYPTIAN YOGA: The Philosophy of Enlightenment is a wonderful resource book which won't become dated and is useful for both neophytes and adepts of the mystical sciences...

—NewAge Retailer Review

Other Books From C M Books

P.O.Box 570459
Miami, Florida, 33257
(305) 378-6253 Fax: (305) 378-6253

This book is part of a series on the study and practice of Ancient Egyptian Yoga and Mystical Spirituality based on the writings of Dr. Muata Abhaya Ashby. They are also part of the Egyptian Yoga Course provided by the Sema Institute of Yoga. Below you will find a listing of the other books in this series. For more information send for the Egyptian Yoga Book-Audio-Video Catalog or the Egyptian Yoga Course Catalog.

Now you can study the teachings of Egyptian and Indian Yoga wisdom and Spirituality with the Egyptian Yoga Mystical Spirituality Series. The Egyptian Yoga Series takes you through the Initiation process and lead you to understand the mysteries of the soul and the Divine and to attain the highest goal of life: ENLIGHTENMENT. The ***Egyptian Yoga Series***, takes you on an in depth study of Ancient Egyptian mythology and their inner mystical meaning. Each Book is prepared for the serious student of the mystical sciences and provides a study of the teachings along with exercises, assignments and projects to make the teachings understood and effective in real life. The Series is part of the Egyptian Yoga course but may be purchased even if you are not taking the course. The series is ideal for study groups.

Prices subject to change.

1.   EGYPTIAN YOGA: THE PHILOSOPHY OF ENLIGHTENMENT An original, fully illustrated work, including hieroglyphs, detailing the meaning of the Egyptian mysteries, tantric yoga, psycho-spiritual and physical exercises. Egyptian Yoga is a guide to the practice of the highest spiritual philosophy which leads to absolute freedom from human misery and to immortality. It is well known by scholars that Egyptian philosophy is the basis of Western and Middle Eastern religious philosophies such as *Christianity, Islam, Judaism,* the *Kabala,* and Greek philosophy, but what about Indian philosophy, Yoga and Taoism? What were the original teachings? How can they be practiced today? What is the source of pain and suffering in the world and what is the solution? Discover the deepest mysteries of the mind and universe within and outside of your self. 8.5" X 11" ISBN: 1-884564-01-1 Soft $19.95

2.   EGYPTIAN YOGA II: The Supreme Wisdom of Enlightenment by Dr. Muata Ashby ISBN 1-884564-39-9 $23.95 U.S. In this long awaited sequel to *Egyptian Yoga: The Philosophy of Enlightenment* you will take a fascinating and enlightening journey back in time and discover the teachings which constituted the epitome of Ancient Egyptian spiritual wisdom. What are the disciplines which lead to the fulfillment of all desires? Delve into the three states of consciousness (waking, dream and deep sleep) and the fourth state which transcends them all, Neberdjer, "The Absolute." These teachings of the city of Waset (Thebes) were the crowning achievement of the Sages of Ancient Egypt. They establish the standard mystical keys for understanding the profound

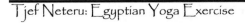

mystical symbolism of the Triad of human consciousness.

3. THE KEMETIC DIET: GUIDE TO HEALTH, DIET AND FASTING Health issues have always been important to human beings since the beginning of time. The earliest records of history show that the art of healing was held in high esteem since the time of Ancient Egypt. In the early 20th century, medical doctors had almost attained the status of sainthood by the promotion of the idea that they alone were "scientists" while other healing modalities and traditional healers who did not follow the "scientific method' were nothing but superstitious, ignorant charlatans who at best would take the money of their clients and at worst kill them with the unscientific "snake oils" and "irrational theories". In the late 20th century, the failure of the modern medical establishment's ability to lead the general public to good health, promoted the move by many in society towards "alternative medicine". Alternative medicine disciplines are those healing modalities which do not adhere to the philosophy of allopathic medicine. Allopathic medicine is what medical doctors practice by an large. It is the theory that disease is caused by agencies outside the body such as bacteria, viruses or physical means which affect the body. These can therefore be treated by medicines and therapies The natural healing method began in the absence of extensive technologies with the idea that all the answers for health may be found in nature or rather, the deviation from nature. Therefore, the health of the body can be restored by correcting the aberration and thereby restoring balance. This is the area that will be covered in this volume. Allopathic techniques have their place in the art of healing. However, we should not forget that the body is a grand achievement of the spirit and built into it is the capacity to maintain itself and heal itself. Ashby, Muata ISBN: 1-884564-49-6 $28.95

4. INITIATION INTO EGYPTIAN YOGA Shedy: Spiritual discipline or program, to go deeply into the mysteries, to study the mystery teachings and literature profoundly, to penetrate the mysteries. You will learn about the mysteries of initiation into the teachings and practice of Yoga and how to become an Initiate of the mystical sciences. This insightful manual is the first in a series which introduces you to the goals of daily spiritual and yoga practices:

Meditation, Diet, Words of Power and the ancient wisdom teachings. 8.5" X 11" ISBN 1-884564-02-X Soft Cover $24.95 U.S.

5. *THE AFRICAN ORIGINS OF CIVILIZATION, MYSTICAL RELIGION AND YOGA PHILOSOPHY* HARD COVER EDITION ISBN: 1-884564-50-X $80.00 U.S. 81/2" X 11" Part 1, Part 2, Part 3 in one volume 683 Pages Hard Cover First Edition Three volumes in one. Over the past several years I have been asked to put together in one volume the most important evidences showing the correlations and common teachings between Kamitan (Ancient Egyptian) culture and religion and that of India. The questions of the history of Ancient Egypt, and the latest archeological evidences showing civilization and culture in Ancient Egypt and its spread to other countries, has intrigued many scholars as well as mystics over the years. Also, the possibility that Ancient Egyptian Priests and Priestesses migrated to Greece, India and other countries to carry on the traditions of the Ancient Egyptian Mysteries, has been speculated over the years as well. In chapter 1 of the book *Egyptian Yoga The Philosophy of Enlightenment,* 1995, I first introduced the deepest comparison between Ancient Egypt and India that had been brought forth up to that time. Now, in the year 2001 this new book, *THE AFRICAN ORIGINS OF CIVILIZATION, MYSTICAL RELIGION AND YOGA PHILOSOPHY,* more fully explores the motifs, symbols and philosophical correlations between Ancient Egyptian and Indian mysticism and clearly shows not only that Ancient Egypt and India were connected culturally but also spiritually. How does this knowledge help the spiritual aspirant? This discovery has great importance for the Yogis and mystics who follow the philosophy of Ancient Egypt and the mysticism of India. It means that India has a longer history and heritage than was previously understood. It shows that the mysteries of Ancient Egypt were essentially a yoga tradition which did not die but rather developed into the modern day systems of Yoga technology of India. It further shows that African culture developed Yoga Mysticism earlier than any other civilization in history. All of this expands our understanding of the unity of culture and the deep legacy of Yoga, which stretches into the distant past, beyond the Indus Valley civilization, the earliest known high culture in India as well as the Vedic tradition of Aryan culture. Therefore, Yoga culture and

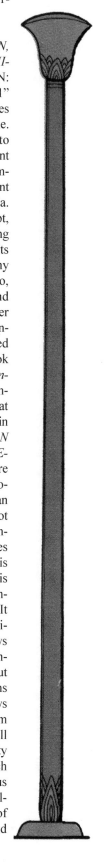

mysticism is the oldest known tradition of spiritual development and Indian mysticism is an extension of the Ancient Egyptian mysticism. By understanding the legacy which Ancient Egypt gave to India the mysticism of India is better understood and by comprehending the heritage of Indian Yoga, which is rooted in Ancient Egypt the Mysticism of Ancient Egypt is also better understood. This expanded understanding allows us to prove the underlying kinship of humanity, through the common symbols, motifs and philosophies which are not disparate and confusing teachings but in reality expressions of the same study of truth through metaphysics and mystical realization of Self. (HARD COVER)

6. AFRICAN ORIGINS BOOK 1 PART 1 African Origins of African Civilization, Religion, Yoga Mysticism and Ethics Philosophy-<u>Soft Cover</u> $24.95 ISBN: 1-884564-55-0

7. AFRICAN ORIGINS BOOK 2 PART 2 African Origins of Western Civilization, Religion and Philosophy(Soft) -<u>Soft Cover</u> $24.95 ISBN: 1-884564-56-9

8. EGYPT AND INDIA (AFRICAN ORIGINS BOOK 3 PART 3) African Origins of Eastern Civilization, Religion, Yoga Mysticism and Philosophy-<u>Soft Cover</u> $29.95 (Soft) ISBN: 1-884564-57-7

9. THE MYSTERIES OF ISIS: **The Ancient Egyptian Philosophy of Self-Realization** - There are several paths to discover the Divine and the mysteries of the higher Self. This volume details the mystery teachings of the goddess Aset (Isis) from Ancient Egypt- the path of wisdom. It includes the teachings of her temple and the disciplines that are enjoined for the initiates of the temple of Aset as they were given in ancient times. Also, this book includes the teachings of the main myths of Aset that lead a human being to spiritual enlightenment and immortality. Through the study of ancient myth and the illumination of initiatic understanding the idea of God is expanded from the mythological comprehension to the metaphysical. Then this metaphysical understanding is related to you, the student, so as to begin understanding your true divine nature. ISBN 1-884564-24-0 $22.99

10. EGYPTIAN PROVERBS: TEMT TCHAAS

11. *Temt Tchaas* means: collection of ——Ancient Egyptian Proverbs How to live according t[ ] MAAT Philosophy. Beginning Meditation. A [ ] proverbs are indexed for easy searches. For th[ ] first time in one volume, ——Ancient Egyptia[ ] Proverbs, wisdom teachings and meditation[ ] fully illustrated with hieroglyphic text and sym[ ]bols. EGYPTIAN PROVERBS is a unique col[ ]lection of knowledge and wisdom which yo[ ] can put into practice today and transform you[ ] life. 5.5"x 8.5" $14.95 U.S ISBN: 1[ ] 884564-00-3

THE PATH OF DIVINE LOVE The Process o[ ] Mystical Transformation and The Path of Di[ ]vine Love This Volume focuses on the an[ ]cient wisdom teachings of "Neter Merri" –th[ ] Ancient Egyptian philosophy of Divine Lov[ ] and how to use them in a scientific process fo[ ] self-transformation. Love is one of the mo[ ]powerful human emotions. It is also the sourc[ ] of Divine feeling that unifies God and the ind[ ]vidual human being. When love is fragmente[ ] and diminished by egoism the Divine connec[ ]tion is lost. The Ancient tradition of Net[ ] Merri leads human beings back to their Divin[ ] connection, allowing them to discover their in[ ]nate glorious self that is actually Divine an[ ] immortal. This volume will detail the process o[ ] transformation from ordinary consciousness t[ ] cosmic consciousness through the integrate[ ] practice of the teachings and the path of Devo[ ]tional Love toward the Divine. 5.5"x 8.5[ ] ISBN 1-884564-11-9 $22.99

12. INTRODUCTION TO MAAT PHILOSOPHY[ ] Spiritual Enlightenment Through the Path o[ ] Virtue Known as Karma Yoga in India, th[ ] teachings of MAAT for living virtuously an[ ] with orderly wisdom are explained and the stu[ ]dent is to begin practicing the precepts of Maa[ ] in daily life so as to promote the process of pu[ ]rification of the heart in preparation for th[ ] judgment of the soul. This judgment will b[ ] understood not as an event that will occur at th[ ] time of death but as an event that occurs con[ ]tinuously, at every moment in the life of th[ ] individual. The student will learn how to be[ ]come allied with the forces of the Higher Se[ ] and to thereby begin cleansing the mind (hear[ ] of impurities so as to attain a higher vision o[ ] reality. ISBN 1-884564-20-8 $22.99

13. MEDITATION The Ancient Egyptian Path t[ ] Enlightenment Many people do not kno[ ]

about the rich history of meditation practice in Ancient Egypt. This volume outlines the theory of meditation and presents the Ancient Egyptian Hieroglyphic text which give instruction as to the nature of the mind and its three modes of expression. It also presents the texts which give instruction on the practice of meditation for spiritual Enlightenment and unity with the Divine. This volume allows the reader to begin practicing meditation by explaining, in easy to understand terms, the simplest form of meditation and working up to the most advanced form which was practiced in ancient times and which is still practiced by yogis around the world in modern times. ISBN 1-884564-27-7 $24.99

14. THE GLORIOUS LIGHT MEDITATION TECHNIQUE OF ANCIENT EGYPT ISBN: 1-884564-15-1$14.95 (PB) New for the year 2000. This volume is based on the earliest known instruction in history given for the practice of formal meditation. Discovered by Dr. Muata Ashby, it is inscribed on the walls of the Tomb of Seti I in Thebes Egypt. This volume details the philosophy and practice of this unique system of meditation originated in Ancient Egypt and the earliest practice of meditation known in the world which occurred in the most advanced African Culture.

15. THE SERPENT POWER: The Ancient Egyptian Mystical Wisdom of the Inner Life Force. This Volume specifically deals with the latent life Force energy of the universe and in the human body, its control and sublimation. How to develop the Life Force energy of the subtle body. This Volume will introduce the esoteric wisdom of the science of how virtuous living acts in a subtle and mysterious way to cleanse the latent psychic energy conduits and vortices of the spiritual body. ISBN 1-884564-19-4 $22.95

16. EGYPTIAN YOGA MEDITATION IN MOTION Thef Neteru: *The Movement of The Gods and Goddesses* Discover the physical postures and exercises practiced thousands of years ago in Ancient Egypt which are today known as Yoga exercises. This work is based on the pictures and teachings from the Creation story of Ra, The Asarian Resurrection Myth and the carvings and reliefs from various Temples in Ancient Egypt 8.5" X 11" ISBN 1-884564-10-0 Soft Cover $18.99 Exercise video $21.99

17. EGYPTIAN TANTRA YOGA: The Art of Sex Sublimation and Universal Consciousness This Volume will expand on the male and female principles within the human body and in the universe and further detail the sublimation of sexual energy into spiritual energy. The student will study the deities Min and Hathor, Asar and Aset, Geb and Nut and discover the mystical implications for a practical spiritual discipline. This Volume will also focus on the Tantric aspects of Ancient Egyptian and Indian mysticism, the purpose of sex and the mystical teachings of sexual sublimation which lead to self-knowledge and Enlightenment. 5.5"x 8.5" ISBN 1-884564-03-8 $24.95

18. ASARIAN RELIGION: RESURRECTING OSIRIS The path of Mystical Awakening and the Keys to Immortality NEW REVISED AND EXPANDED EDITION! The Ancient Sages created stories based on human and superhuman beings whose struggles, aspirations, needs and desires ultimately lead them to discover their true Self. The myth of Aset, Asar and Heru is no exception in this area. While there is no one source where the entire story may be found, pieces of it are inscribed in various ancient Temples walls, tombs, steles and papyri. For the first time available, the complete myth of Asar, Aset and Heru has been compiled from original Ancient Egyptian, Greek and Coptic Texts. This epic myth has been richly illustrated with reliefs from the Temple of Heru at Edfu, the Temple of Aset at Philae, the Temple of Asar at Abydos, the Temple of Hathor at Denderah and various papyri, inscriptions and reliefs. Discover the myth which inspired the teachings of the *Shetaut Neter* (Egyptian Mystery System - Egyptian Yoga) and the Egyptian Book of Coming Forth By Day. Also, discover the three levels of Ancient Egyptian Religion, how to understand the mysteries of the Duat or Astral World and how to discover the abode of the Supreme in the Amenta, *The Other World* The ancient religion of Asar, Aset and Heru, if properly understood, contains all of the elements necessary to lead the sincere aspirant to attain immortality through inner self-discovery. This volume presents the entire myth and explores the main mystical themes and rituals associated with the myth for understating human existence, creation and the way to achieve spiritual emancipation - *Resurrection.* The Asarian myth is so powerful that it influenced and is still

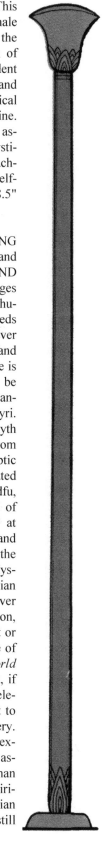

having an effect on the major world religions. Discover the origins and mystical meaning of the Christian Trinity, the Eucharist ritual and the ancient origin of the birthday of Jesus Christ. Soft Cover ISBN: 1-884564-27-5 $24.95

19. **THE EGYPTIAN BOOK OF THE DEAD** MYSTICISM OF THE PERT EM HERU $26.95 ISBN# 1-884564-28-3 Size: 8½" X 11" I Know myself, I know myself, I am One With God!–From the Pert Em Heru "The Ru Pert em Heru" or "Ancient Egyptian Book of The Dead," or "Book of Coming Forth By Day" as it is more popularly known, has fascinated the world since the successful translation of Ancient Egyptian hieroglyphic scripture over 150 years ago. The astonishing writings in it reveal that the Ancient Egyptians believed in life after death and in an ultimate destiny to discover the Divine. The elegance and aesthetic beauty of the hieroglyphic text itself has inspired many see it as an art form in and of itself. But is there more to it than that? Did the Ancient Egyptian wisdom contain more than just aphorisms and hopes of eternal life beyond death? In this volume Dr. Muata Ashby, the author of over 25 books on Ancient Egyptian Yoga Philosophy has produced a new translation of the original texts which uncovers a mystical teaching underlying the sayings and rituals instituted by the Ancient Egyptian Sages and Saints. "Once the philosophy of Ancient Egypt is understood as a mystical tradition instead of as a religion or primitive mythology, it reveals its secrets which if practiced today will lead anyone to discover the glory of spiritual self-discovery. The Pert em Heru is in every way comparable to the Indian Upanishads or the Tibetan Book of the Dead." ˜ Muata Abhaya Ashby

20. ANUNIAN THEOLOGY THE MYSTERIES OF RA The Philosophy of Anu and The Mystical Teachings of The Ancient Egyptian Creation Myth Discover the mystical teachings contained in the Creation Myth and the gods and goddesses who brought creation and human beings into existence. The Creation Myth holds the key to understanding the universe and for attaining spiritual Enlightenment. ISBN: 1-884564-38-0 40 pages $14.95

21. MYSTERIES OF MIND AND MEMPHITE THEOLOGY Mysticism of Ptah, Egyptian

Physics and Yoga Metaphysics and the Hidden properties of Matter This Volume will go deeper into the philosophy of God as creation and will explore the concepts of modern science and how they correlate with ancient teachings This Volume will lay the ground work for the understanding of the philosophy of universal consciousness and the initiatic/yogic insight into who or what is God? ISBN 1-884564-07-0 $21.95

22. THE GODDESS AND THE EGYPTIAN MYSTERIESTHE PATH OF THE GODDESS THE GODDESS PATH The Secret Forms of the Goddess and the Rituals of Resurrection The Supreme Being may be worshipped as father or as mother. *Ushet Rekhat* or *Mother Worship*, is the spiritual process of worshipping the Divine in the form of the Divine Goddess. It celebrates the most important forms of the Goddess including *Nathor, Maat, Aset, Arat, Amentet and Hathor* and explores their mystical meaning as well as the rising of *Sirius,* the star of Aset (Aset) and the new birth of Hor (Heru) The end of the year is a time of reckoning, reflection and engendering a new or renewed positive movement toward attaining spiritual Enlightenment. The Mother Worship devotional meditation ritual, performed on five days during the month of December and on New Year's Eve, is based on the Ushet Rekhit. During the ceremony, the cosmic forces, symbolized by Sirius - and the constellation of Orion --, are harnessed through the understanding and devotional attitude of the participant. This propitiation draws the light of wisdom and health to all those who share in the ritual, leading to prosperity and wisdom. $14.95 ISBN 1 884564-18-6

23. *THE MYSTICAL JOURNEY FROM JESUS TO CHRIST* $24.95 ISBN# 1-884564-05-4 size: 8½" X 11" Discover the ancient Egyptian origins of Christianity before the Catholic Church and learn the mystical teachings given by Jesus to assist all humanity in becoming Christlike. Discover the secret meaning of the Gospels that were discovered in Egypt. Also discover how and why so many Christian churches came into being. Discover that the Bible still holds the keys to mystical realization even though its original writings were changed by the church. Discover how to practice the original teachings of Christianity which leads to the Kingdom of Heaven.

24. THE STORY OF ASAR, ASET AND HERU: An Ancient Egyptian Legend (For Children) Now for the first time, the most ancient myth of Ancient Egypt comes alive for children. Inspired by the books *The Asarian Resurrection: The Ancient Egyptian Bible* and *The Mystical Teachings of The Asarian Resurrection, The Story of Asar, Aset and Heru* is an easy to understand and thrilling tale which inspired the children of Ancient Egypt to aspire to greatness and righteousness. If you and your child have enjoyed stories like *The Lion King* and *Star Wars you will love The Story of Asar, Aset and Heru.* Also, if you know the story of Jesus and Krishna you will discover than Ancient Egypt had a similar myth and that this myth carries important spiritual teachings for living a fruitful and fulfilling life. This book may be used along with *The Parents Guide To The Asarian Resurrection Myth: How to Teach Yourself and Your Child the Principles of Universal Mystical Religion.* The guide provides some background to the Asarian Resurrection myth and it also gives insight into the mystical teachings contained in it which you may introduce to your child. It is designed for parents who wish to grow spiritually with their children and it serves as an introduction for those who would like to study the Asarian Resurrection Myth in depth and to practice its teachings. 41 pages 8.5" X 11" ISBN: 1-884564-31-3 $12.95

25. THE PARENTS GUIDE TO THE AUSARIAN RESURRECTION MYTH: How to Teach Yourself and Your Child the Principles of Universal Mystical Religion. This insightful manual brings for the timeless wisdom of the ancient through the Ancient Egyptian myth of Asar, Aset and Heru and the mystical teachings contained in it for parents who want to guide their children to understand and practice the teachings of mystical spirituality. This manual may be used with the children's storybook *The Story of Asar, Aset and Heru* by Dr. Muata Abhaya Ashby. 5.5"x 8.5" ISBN: 1-884564-30-5 $14.95

26. HEALING THE CRIMINAL HEART BOOK 1 Introduction to Maat Philosophy, Yoga and Spiritual Redemption Through the Path of Virtue Who is a criminal? Is there such a thing as a criminal heart? What is the source of evil and sinfulness and is there any way to rise above it? Is there redemption for those who have committed sins, even the worst crimes? Ancient Egyptian mystical psychology holds important answers to these questions. Over ten thousand years ago mystical psychologists, the Sages of Ancient Egypt, studied and charted the human mind and spirit and laid out a path which will lead to spiritual redemption, prosperity and Enlightenment. This introductory volume brings forth the teachings of the Asarian Resurrection, the most important myth of Ancient Egypt, with relation to the faults of human existence: anger, hatred, greed, lust, animosity, discontent, ignorance, egoism jealousy, bitterness, and a myriad of psycho-spiritual ailments which keep a human being in a state of negativity and adversity. 5.5"x 8.5" ISBN: 1-884564-17-8 $15.95

27. THEATER & DRAMA OF THE ANCIENT EGYPTIAN MYSTERIES: Featuring the Ancient Egyptian stage play-"The Enlightenment of Hathor' Based on an Ancient Egyptian Drama, The original Theater -Mysticism of the Temple of Hetheru $14.95 By Dr. Muata Ashby

28. GUIDE TO PRINT ON DEMAND: SELF-PUBLISH FOR PROFIT, SPIRITUAL FULFILLMENT AND SERVICE TO HUMANITY Everyone asks us how we produced so many books in such a short time. Here are the secrets to writing and producing books that uplift humanity and how to get them printed for a fraction of the regular cost. Anyone can become an author even if they have limited funds. All that is necessary is the willingness to learn how the printing and book business work and the desire to follow the special instructions given here for preparing your manuscript format. Then you take your work directly to the non-traditional companies who can produce your books for less than the traditional book printer can. ISBN: 1-884564-40-2 $16.95 U. S.

29. Egyptian Mysteries: Vol. 1, Shetaut Neter ISBN: 1-884564-41-0 $19.99 What are the Mysteries? For thousands of years the spiritual tradition of Ancient Egypt, *Shetaut Neter,* "The Egyptian Mysteries," "The Secret Teachings," have fascinated, tantalized and amazed the world. At one time exalted and recognized as the highest culture of the world, by Africans, Europeans, Asiatics, Hindus, Buddhists and other cultures of the ancient world, in time it was shunned by the emerging orthodox world religions. Its temples desecrated, its philosophy

maligned, its tradition spurned, its philosophy dormant in the mystical *Medu Neter*, the mysterious hieroglyphic texts which hold the secret symbolic meaning that has scarcely been discerned up to now. What are the secrets of *Nehast* {spiritual awakening and emancipation, resurrection}. More than just a literal translation, this volume is for awakening to the secret code *Shetitu* of the teaching which was not deciphered by Egyptologists, nor could be understood by ordinary spiritualists. This book is a reinstatement of the original science made available for our times, to the reincarnated followers of Ancient Egyptian culture and the prospect of spiritual freedom to break the bonds of *Khemn*, "ignorance," and slavery to evil forces: *Såaa* .

30. EGYPTIAN MYSTERIES VOL 2: Dictionary of Gods and Goddesses ISBN: 1-884564-23-2 $21.95 This book is about the mystery of neteru, the gods and goddesses of Ancient Egypt (Kamit, Kemet). Neteru means "Gods and Goddesses." But the Neterian teaching of Neteru represents more than the usual limited modern day concept of "divinities" or "spirits." The Neteru of Kamit are also metaphors, cosmic principles and vehicles for the enlightening teachings of Shetaut Neter (Ancient Egyptian-African Religion). Actually they are the elements for one of the most advanced systems of spirituality ever conceived in human history. Understanding the concept of neteru provides a firm basis for spiritual evolution and the pathway for viable culture, peace on earth and a healthy human society. Why is it important to have gods and goddesses in our lives? In order for spiritual evolution to be possible, once a human being has accepted that there is existence after death and there is a transcendental being who exists beyond time and space knowledge, human beings need a connection to that which transcends the ordinary experience of human life in time and space and a means to understand the transcendental reality beyond the mundane reality.

31. EGYPTIAN MYSTERIES VOL. 3 The Priests and Priestesses of Ancient Egypt ISBN: 1-884564-53-4 $22.95 This volume details the path of Neterian priesthood, the joys, challenges and rewards of advanced Neterian life, the teachings that allowed the priests and priestesses to manage the most long lived civilization in human history and how that path can b[e] adopted today; for those who want to tread th[e] path of the Clergy of Shetaut Neter.

32. THE KING OF EGYPT: The Struggle of Goo[d] and Evil for Control of the World and The Hu[-]man Soul ISBN 1-8840564-44-5 $18.95 Thi[s] volume contains a novelized version of th[e] Asarian Resurrection myth that is based on th[e] actual scriptures presented in the Book Asaria[n] Religion (old name –Resurrecting Osiris). Thi[s] volume is prepared in the form of a screenpla[y] and can be easily adapted to be used as a stag[e] play. Spiritual seeking is a mythic journey tha[t] has many emotional highs and lows, ecstasie[s] and depressions, victories and frustrations. Thi[s] is the War of Life that is played out in the myt[h] as the struggle of Heru and Set and those an[d] mythic characters that represent the huma[n] Higher and Lower self. How to understand th[e] war and emerge victorious in the journey o life[?] The ultimate victory and fulfillment can be ex[-]perienced, which is not changeable or lost i[n] time. The purpose of myth is to convey the wis[-]dom of life through the story of divinities wh[o] show the way to overcome the challenges an[d] foibles of life. In this volume the feelings an[d] emotions of the characters of the myth hav[e] been highlighted to show the deeply rich textur[e] of the Ancient Egyptian myth. This myth co[n-]tains deep spiritual teachings and insights int[o] the nature of self, of God and the mysteries [of] life and the means to discover the true meanin[g] of life and thereby achieve the true purpose [of] life. To become victorious in the battle of lif[e] means to become the King (or Queen) of Egyp[t]. Have you seen movies like The Lion King[,] Hamlet, The Odyssey, or The Little Buddha[?] These have been some of the most popula[r] movies in modern times. The Sema Institute [of] Yoga is dedicated to researching and presentin[g] the wisdom and culture of ancient Africa. Th[e] Script is designed to be produced as a motio[n] picture but may be addapted for the theater a[s] well. $19.95 copyright 1998 By Dr. Mua[ta] Ashby

33. FROM EGYPT TO GREECE: The Kamita[n] Origins of Greek Culture and Religion ISBN: [1-]884564-47-X $22.95 U.S. FROM EGYPT T[O] GREECE This insightful manual is a quic[k] reference to Ancient Egyptian mythology an[d] philosophy and its correlation to what late[r] became known as Greek and Rome mytholog[y] and philosophy. It outlines the basic tenets [of]

the mythologies and shoes the ancient origins of Greek culture in Ancient Egypt. This volume also acts as a resource for Colleges students who would like to set up fraternities and sororities based on the original Ancient Egyptian principles of Sheti and Maat philosophy. ISBN: 1-884564-47-X $22.95 U. S.

34. THE FORTY TWO PRECEPTS OF MAAT, THE   PHILOSOPHY   OF   RIGHTEOUS ACTION AND THE ANCIENT EGYPTIAN WISDOM TEXTS <u>ADVANCED STUDIES</u> This manual is designed for use with the 1998 Maat Philosophy Class conducted by Dr. Muata Ashby. This is a detailed study of Maat Philosophy. It contains a compilation of the 42 laws or precepts of Maat and the corresponding principles which they represent along with the teachings of the ancient Egyptian Sages relating to each. Maat philosophy was the basis of Ancient Egyptian society and government as well as the heart of Ancient Egyptian myth and spirituality. Maat is at once a goddess, a cosmic force and a living social doctrine, which promotes social harmony and thereby paves the way for spiritual evolution in all levels of society. ISBN: 1-884564-48-8 $16.95 U.S.

Music Based on the Prt M Hru and other Kemetic Texts

Available on Compact Disc $14.99 and Audio Cassette $9.99

Adorations to the Goddess

Music for Worship of the Goddess

**NEW Egyptian Yoga Music CD
by Sehu Maa
Ancient Egyptian Music CD**
Instrumental Music played on reproductions of Ancient Egyptian Instruments– Ideal for <u>meditation</u> and reflection on the Divine and for the practice of spiritual programs and <u>Yoga exercise sessions.</u>

©1999 By Muata Ashby
CD $14.99 –

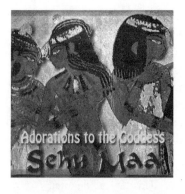

MERIT'S INSPIRATION
**NEW Egyptian Yoga Music CD
by Sehu Maa
Ancient Egyptian Music CD**
Instrumental Music played on reproductions of Ancient Egyptian Instruments– Ideal for <u>meditation</u> and reflection on the Divine and for the practice of spiritual programs and <u>Yoga exercise sessions.</u>
©1999 By
Muata Ashby
CD $14.99 –
UPC# 761527100429

ANORATIONS TO RA AND HETHERU
**NEW Egyptian Yoga Music CD
By Sehu Maa (Muata Ashby)
Based on the Words of Power of Ra and HetHeru**
played on reproductions of Ancient Egyptian Instruments **Ancient Egyptian Instruments used: Voice, Clapping, Nefer Lute, Tar Drum, Sistrums, Cymbals** – The Chants, Devotions, Rhythms and Festive Songs Of the Neteru – Ideal for meditation, and devotional singing and dancing.
©1999 By Muata Ashby
CD $14.99 –
UPC# 761527100221

SONGS TO ASAR ASET AND HERU
**NEW
Egyptian Yoga Music CD
By Sehu Maa**
played on reproductions of Ancient Egyptian Instruments– The Chants, Devotions, Rhythms and Festive Songs Of the Neteru - Ideal for meditation, and devo-

tional singing and dancing.
Based on the Words of Power of Asar (Asar), Aset (Aset) and Heru (Heru) Om Asar Aset Heru is the third in a series of musical explorations of the Kemetic (Ancient Egyptian) tradition of music. Its ideas are based on the Ancient Egyptian Religion of Asar, Aset and Heru and it s designed for listening, meditation and worship. ©1999 By Muata Ashby

CD $14.99 –
UPC# 761527100122

HAARI OM: ANCIENT EGYPT MEETS INDIA IN MUSIC
NEW Music CD
By Sehu Maa

The Chants, Devotions, Rhythms and Festive Songs Of the Ancient Egypt and India, harmonized and played on reproductions of ancient instruments along with modern instruments and beats. Ideal for meditation, and devotional singing and dancing.
Haari Om is the fourth in a series of musical explorations of the Kemetic (Ancient Egyptian) and Indian traditions of music, chanting and devotional spiritual practice. Its ideas are based on the Ancient Egyptian Yoga spirituality and Indian Yoga spirituality.
©1999 By Muata Ashby
CD $14.99 –
UPC# 761527100528

RA AKHU: THE GLORIOUS LIGHT
NEW
Egyptian Yoga Music CD
By Sehu Maa
The fifth collection of original music compositions based on the Teachings and Words of The Trinity, the God Asar and the Goddess Nebethet, the Divinity Aten, the God Heru, and the Special Meditation Hekau or Words of Power of Ra from the Ancient Egyptian Tomb of Seti I and more...
played on reproductions of Ancient Egyptian Instruments and modern instruments - **Ancient Egyptian Instruments used: Voice, Clapping, Nefer Lute, Tar Drum, Sistrums, Cymbals**
– The Chants, Devotions, Rhythms and Festive Songs Of the Neteru – Ideal for meditation, and devotional singing and dancing.
©1999 By Muata Ashby
CD $14.99 –
UPC# 761527100825

GLORIES OF THE DIVINE MOTHER
Based on the hieroglyphic text of the worship of Goddess Net.
The Glories of The Great Mother
©2000 Muata Ashby
CD $14.99 UPC# 761527101129`

ABOUT

Dr. Muata Ashby

Reginald Muata Ashby was born in New York City but grew up in the Caribbean. Displaying an early interest in ancient civilizations and the Humanities, he began to study these subjects while in college but put these aside to work in the business world. After successfully running a business with his wife for several years they decided to pursue a deeper movement in life. Mr. Ashby began studies in the area of religion and philosophy and achieved doctorates in these areas while at the same time he began to collect his research into what would later become several books on the subject of the origins of Yoga Philosophy and practice in ancient Africa (Ancient Egypt) and also the origins of Christian Mysticism in Ancient Egypt.

Reginald Muata Ashby holds a Doctor of Philosophy Degree in Religion, and a Doctor of Divinity Degree in Holistic Healing. He is also a Pastoral Counselor and Teacher of Yoga Philosophy and Discipline. Dr. Ashby received his Doctor of Divinity Degree from and is an adjunct faculty member of the American Institute of Holistic Theology. Dr. Ashby is a certification as a PREP Relationship Counselor. Dr. Ashby has been an independent researcher and practitioner of Egyptian, Indian and Chinese Yoga and psychology as well as Christian Mysticism. Dr. Ashby has engaged in Post Graduate research in advanced Jnana, Bhakti and Kundalini Yogas at the Yoga Research Foundation under the direction of Swami Jyotirmayananda. He has extensively studied mystical religious traditions from around the world and is an accomplished lecturer, artist, poet, screenwriter, playwright and author of over 25 books on yoga and spiritual philosophy. He is an Ordained Minister and Spiritual Counselor and also the founder the Sema Institute, a non-profit organization dedicated to spreading the wisdom of Yoga and the Ancient Egyptian mystical traditions.

Who is Hemt Neter Dr. Karen Vijaya Clarke-Ashby?

Karen Clarke-Ashby (Seba Dja) is a Kamitan (Kamitan) priestess, and an independent researcher, practitioner and teacher of Sema (Smai) Tawi (Kamitan) and Indian Integral Yoga Systems, a Doctor of Veterinary Medicine, a Pastoral Spiritual Counselor, a Pastoral Health and Nutrition Counselor, and a Sema (Smai) Tawi Life-style Consultant." Dr. Ashby has engaged in post-graduate research in advanced Jnana, Bhakti, Karma, Raja and Kundalini Yogas at the Sema Institute of Yoga and Yoga Research Foundation, and has also worked extensively with her husband and spiritual partner, Dr. Muata Ashby, author of the Egyptian Yoga Book Series, editing many of these books, as well as studying, writing and lecturing in the area of Kamitan Yoga and Spirituality. She is a certified Tjef Neteru Sema Paut (Kamitan Yoga Exercise system) and Indian Hatha Yoga Exercise instructor, the Coordinator and Instructor for the Level 1 Teacher Certification Tjef Neteru Sema Training programs, and a teacher of health and stress management applications of the Yoga / Sema Tawi systems for modern society, based on the Kamitan and/or Indian yogic principles. Also, she is the co-author of "The Egyptian Yoga Exercise Workout Book," a contributing author for "The Kamitan Diet, Food for Body, Mind and Soul," author of the soon to be released, "Yoga Mystic Metaphors for Enlightenment."

Hotep -Peace be with you!

Seba Muata Ashby & Karen Ashby.

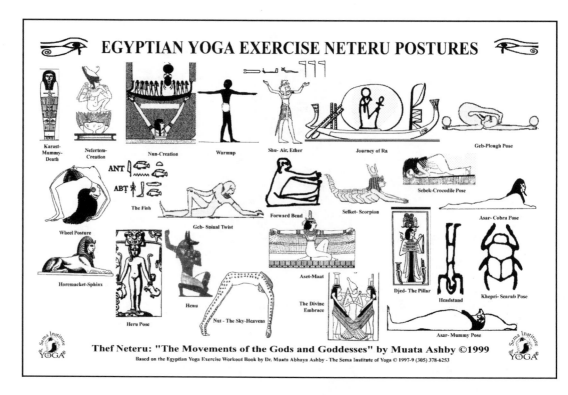

New Official
Egyptian Yoga Exercise Posture Posters
Approx. 11" X 17" Laminated $10.00 each

Order Form

Telephone orders: Call Toll Free: 1(305) 378-6253. Have your AMEX, Optima, Visa or Master-Card ready.

Fax orders: 1-(305) 378-6253

Postal Orders: Sema Institute of Yoga, P.O. Box 570459, Miami, Fl. 33257. USA.

Please send the following books and / or tapes.

ITEM

_____ Cost $_____
_____ Cost $_____
_____ Cost $_____
_____ Cost $_____
_____ Cost $_____
_____ Cost $_____

Shipping: Air Mail or UPS: $6.50 for first book and $.50 for each additional $_____

Sub Total $_____

Name:_____
Address:_____
City:_____ State:_____ Zip:_____

Sales tax: Please add 6.5% for books shipped to Florida addresses

_____Payment:_____
_____Check_____ If paying by check include your drivers
licence number_____ State_____

Tel. #_____

_____Credit card: _____ Visa, _____ MasterCard, _____ Optima,
_____ AMEX.

Card number:_____

Name on card:_____ Exp. date:_____/_____

TO PLACE AN ORDER, contact your local bookstore or send CK or MO for the cost of each item plus shipping and handling to the address below. Shipping cost $6.50 first item, .50¢ each additional item. (Prices subject to change) _Ordering from outside U.S._ send equivalent to U.S. currency plus $5 in U.S. currency for the first item and $3 for each additional for shipping. Send to C.M. Books, P.O. Box 570459, Miami, Fl. 33257 or Visa-Master Card INCLUDE Physical address and Driver's license # if you are sending a check as payment. Bookstores: You may purchase directly from C.M. Books AT 40% DISCOUNT- CALL 305-378-6253 C.M. BOOKS, P.O. BOX 570459, MIAMI, FL. 33257 -

72160322R00107